Barge Building and Barge Builders of the Swale

D.L. SATTIN

MERESBOROUGH BOOKS
1990

Published by Meresborough Books, 17 Station Road, Rainham, Gillingham, Kent. ME8 7RS.

Meresborough Books is a specialist publisher of over 100 books about Kent and of the monthly magazine 'Bygone Kent'. Books available include:

'Just Off the Swale' by Don Sattin. The story of the barge building village of Conyer. £5.95.

'George Bargebrick Esq' by Richard-Hugh Perks. A pictorial record of Smeed Deans of Sittingbourne and their colourful founder, George Smeed. Paperback £4.50.

'The Past Glory of Milton Creek' by Alan Cordell and Leslie Williams. £9.95.

'Us Bargemen' by Arthur Bennett. The author's life living on the sailing barge *Henry*. £6.95.

ISBN 0948193 5 30

Printed and bound in Great Britain by
Biddles Ltd, Guildford and King's Lynn

CONTENTS

Acknowledgements

'Bargebuilding on the Swale' is an attempt to put together a short history of barge building in the Swale area. Much has been written about the area in the past; this is an attempt to gather it together in one book. It has been a labour of love trying to find people who could remember the trade further back than myself. I have found few of these and most of the people whom I did manage to find were very old and their memories vague and unreliable.

To the few who did put themselves out to help me I am most grateful; at least they all gave me information which proved very useful and pointed me in the right direction for other information. If I had started this book forty years ago I may have stood a better chance of obtaining the information that I have been searching for. Forty years ago the information was there, stored away in the heads of young men who are now eighty years old or more. So, if you are thinking of writing history, do it now or it will be gone.

About the time that I started this book several friends of mine were also researching along similar lines and have shared some of their findings. I am most grateful to Peter Ferguson, Alan Cordell, Hugh Perks, Pat O'Driscoll, Bob Childs and Tony Ellis.

Mr R.K. Anderson of Whitstable gave me valuable assistance about the Whitstable end, Nobby Wood helped me with the Queenborough end; I would also like to thank C. Cackett Parish Clerk to Queenborough Parish Council for his kindly assistance about the area. My thanks to Marilyn Stansell for typing my manuscripts and to many more too numerous to name who allowed me to interview them or dug out family papers and photos.

My thanks to Glenn Coleman for the drawings, also Jeremy Nesham, Kate and Steve for the computer work, to Basil G. Emmerson for the photo of the late Wally Buchanan.

Wally Buchanan — Master Rigger

After a long illness fighting against cancer Wally Buchanan died on 23rd October 1987. Wally was a quiet spoken man who had travelled the world wherever his work took him. A seaman as well as a rigger, he sailed in some of the ships that he had rigged. Wally and I worked together in the Liverpool Maritime Museum. We were both interested in the same things and were both interested in each other's work.

Working with Wally was always a pleasure. He made hard work look easy and could not abide shirkers or fools. In spite of that he had a wonderful sense of humour which could easily be missed if you were not paying attention.

Whenever I pass *Cutty Sark* I shall look into the rigging with a feeling that I knew a great man who worked up there among the spars and rigging.

Don Sattin

Forest grown oak. The straight bol was used for planks and beams.

A hedgerow oak tree much used for its branches which were sawn into knees for bargebuilding.

Chapter I:
Timbers And Equipment

OAK: Two different oaks are common in Europe. The pendunculate and the sessile. These are also grown in France, Poland and through to Slavonia.

The oak tree attains a height of between 60 and 100 feet. Grown in the open it branches out low down. These are the trees the boatbuilders like. The crooked branches are used for boat knees and breast hooks. Grown under forest conditions it grows a clean straight bole sometimes up to 50 feet in length.

Oak is grown in pure stands in small woods or forests, also in mixed woods where it dominates. It likes warm, moist soil. It is found in Europe south of 60 degrees N, in Great Britain it is commonest in the South and the Midlands; less common the further north one goes. There is hardly any difference between the timber of the two botanical species; the sapwood varies between 1 and 2 inches and is distinct from the heartwood. Home grown oak varies in quality: the bulk of the timber is comparatively hard and also heavy — on average 45 lbs per cubic foot seasoned and about 67 lbs per cubic foot green with 85 per cent moisture content. Oak has an acidic character and therefore tends to accelerate the corrosion of metals: oak also contains tannin and the action of the two against iron turns oak a blue-black colour. Seasoning oak in the air gives it a tendency to crack and split so the ends of the planks should be strapped and ½ inch battens placed between planks when being stacked. It is also advisable to cover the top plank with old shavings or something to keep direct sunlight off its face. Freshly sawn oak tends to split or crack in a few hours and so needs to be protected quickly. Oak seasons slowly and, if forced, distortion may be appreciable. Shrinkage from green to about 12 per cent moisture content is: tangential around 15/16ths inch to the foot or 7.5 per cent, radial about ½ inch to the foot or 4.0 per cent. Between the two varieties of oak there are numerous hybrids which all seem to have about the same strength properties. The bending properties of oak are very good although green oak tends to rupture on the inside of the bend when steamed. Rapid drying after steaming should be avoided. It is best to bend timber with a 25 per cent moisture content.

Oak has been used in all the timber related trades from furniture to ship-building.

A normal sized Douglas Fir in British Colombia. The author with Fred Brown in front.
(Ed. Brown)

ELM: English and Dutch elm grow freely in the British Isles. It is a hedgerow tree and rarely seen in forests, growing mainly in the lowlands and valleys. The Dutch elm grows throughout Great Britain and English elm is found mainly in England and Wales, attaining a height of 120 feet, sometimes as much as 150 feet with diameter in the region of 3 to 5 feet although some have been up to 8 feet. Some of the large trees are often unsound in the centre; usually the bole is clear from 40 to 60 feet. Elm has a clear differentiation between sapwood and heartwood, especially when it is freshly felled.

English and Dutch elm weigh about 34 lbs to the cubic foot seasoned and about 65 lbs to the cubic foot when green at 135 per cent moisture content.

Elm seasons fairly rapidly with marked tendency to distort but little tendency to split. The timber should be carefully stacked and closely spaced lines of battens placed between each plank; heavy weights should be placed on top of the planks to avoid twisting and warping. The shrinkage from green to 12 per cent moisture content is: tangential about 13/16ths inch to the foot or 6.5 per cent, radial about 9/16ths of an inch to the foot or 4.5 per cent.

Not so high in strength as oak, elm bends well tangentially but splits 20 per cent more easily than oak but is more difficult to split radially than oak. Dutch elm is 4.0 per cent tougher than English elm — otherwise the strength properties of the two timbers do not differ materially. Elm is used on sailing barges for chine planks, some of the run planks, the end boards of hatch covers, keels, deadwoods, leeboard fenders and cappings. Leeboard fenders were tapered chocks placed in front of the leeboards to prevent damage when coming alongside other vessels or dock sides.

OREGON PINE: So called in America and in English boatyards, it is sometimes called British Columbian pine as most of it came from B.C., Canada. British Columbia is the province where most of it grows: its correct name is Douglas Fir. The tree attains a height of 150 to 200 feet with a diameter of three to six feet. However, trees are found up to more than 300 feet high and 15 feet in diameter. I have visited Cathedral Avenue on Vancouver Island where the trees are reputed to be nearer 500 feet high and I and four other people sat on a seat that had been cut into one of these enormous trees, specially placed there for the tourist to be photographed in. These Douglas firs are preserved and are looked after by the foresters. A friend of mine was at one time a lumberjack on Vancouver Island and in his time had cut down thousands of these beautiful trees.

The bole is straight and free from branches for about 100 feet or more and it rarely grows more northerly than 55 degrees N, growing on the western slopes of the Rockies right through Wyoming to southern New Mexico and along the Pacific coast.

It is most abundant in British Columbia where I have seen it used for everything from packing cases to houses. Much planting of this tree has been carried out in Great Britain and Europe, New Zealand and Australia.

We used to find this timber very hard on edge tools like saws, planes and chisels; it had a gritty feel about it and caused us to sharpen our tools more frequently. The average weight of seasoned timber is approximately 33 lbs to the cubic foot: the wood is generally straight grained and seasons rapidly but knots tend to loosen and split. Shrinkage: green to 12 per cent moisture content; tangential about ½ inch to the foot or 4.0 per cent, radial about 5/16ths inch to the foot or 2.5 per cent. Douglas fir can bend but not successfully; we used it mostly for bottom planking and sealings, sometimes lining. It also has great strength when used on edge.

I have seen enormous barge loads of this timber moored in the Fraser River in British Columbia, all chipped up for the paper pulp mills on the Fraser River in British Columbia.

AMERICAN PITCH PINE: The trees are confined to a belt of 125 miles along the Atlantic coast and the Gulf States, from south eastern Virginia south to Florida and along the coast to Trinity River in Texas.

The boles are about 100 feet with a diameter of 2 to 3 feet. The American pitch pine shipped to the United Kingdom is much harder than other commercial species of pine.

Seasoned pitch pine weighs between 41 lbs and 43 lbs per cubic foot; it seasons well and can be steamed and bent. Its strength is almost identical to that of Oregon pine. Pitch pine is used for all types of shipbuilding from spars and masts to fitting out cabins.

A large per cent of the world's rosin and turpentine is produced from these pines. Pitch pine used to arrive into this country by ship and, in the old days, was thrown overboard to be made into rafts; many were baulks about 18 inches square which were then poled to the barge yards using the tides whenever possible.

OTHER WOODS: I have heard and read of stories of the wood of fruit trees being used in the building of barges. Knowing the qualities of fruit tree wood from many years of experience, I would say that any self-respecting shipwright would never put such wood into a sailing barge; fruit trees can only produce short lengths of wood which would be of little use in barge building. There are other woods, of course, used in barge yards. We used to plank up swim-head lighters with English larch and certain types of common fir were used for hatches and bulkheads, bunk boards and cabin flooring.

TREENAILS

One of the oldest known methods of fastening planks to timbers of vessels is the treenail, for many years called the trunnel. Marco Polo mentions them when on his travels around the year 1300 but they were known to have been used centuries before. Trunnels were hardwood pegs varying in size according to their use. Those used on barge work were usually 1⅛ inch diameter and of oak.

The best trunnels were those made from the butts of the oak tree where the wood was always tougher, split out to ensure a straight grain then eight sided with a side axe. They were cut out by eye, large enough to moot down to 1⅛ inch diameter and were from 9 to 16 inches long for barge building. Very few barge yards made their own at the end of the era; firms specialised in supplying them in their eight sided form. They were never mooted until they were wanted in case they shrank and they were delivered in sacks of 100 or 200 depending upon their length. Once received, they would be laid out on racks to season. When trunnels were wanted they were brought to the workbench which had a large leg vice attached to one end; the unmooted trunnels were stacked on the end of the bench close to the vice. A trunnel was then gripped in the vice by about one inch of its length, a tool called a moot would then be entered on the other end and turned clockwise until it touched the vice. By this time, enough of the rounded trunnel would be protruding from the moot; the vice was then released and the moot, with the partly rounded trunnel still in it, would be turned around and the rounded piece of trunnel gripped in the vice. This put the moot in a reverse position so that one could grip the handles of the moot and, pulling towards oneself, turn it anti-clockwise until the moot left the trunnel. This sounds a complicated job but, in fact, it was the reverse and was usually done at piecework rates about one penny farthing a score (old currency). The first day at it, your arms ached — the moot was of cast iron and weighed about 6 lbs or more and the twisting about in the vice holding the weight in one hand while you tightened the vice up with the other made one arm ache more than the other. The mooted trunnels were thrown on to the floor and by the end of the day the floor area would be fairly well covered and anyone who was on piece work was not going to bother about collecting them up. At one time, we had working at Conyer an older shipwright who cycled some five miles from Faversham every day. He liked to be the first to arrive at work and was annoyed if anyone was there ahead of him. On arrival at the yard, he would light the Tilley lamps — very modern in those days — which were always put on the bench before going home at night. This particular morning he arrived just in front of another employee and, in his haste to be first in, he rushed into the shed forgetting the trunnels. He stepped on them and was rocketed almost the length of the shed on this bed of round trunnels. In the complete darkness, no one saw his predicament but this did not lessen his wrath.

The moot was adjustable. The first trunnel to be mooted was driven to see if it was tight enough or too tight. Alterations were then made until the size was correct. Some trunnels went sere* in seasoning and had to be thrown out for burning. At some yards, they rounded their trunnels by driving them through a steel plate which had a hole drilled to the right size; this was quite all right if the man who was doing the driving had a good eye, otherwise many were spoilt by being broken or split. Another thing against this method was the fact that the size could not be varied.

COPPERS AND HOT STUFF
Where barges were built, there had to be some method of boiling tar and pitch together to make what we called 'hot stuff'. In small yards, it may have been outside in a makeshift copper supported on bricks with a fire underneath; a fire risk that the builder was willing to take out in the open away from the building area. At White's Conyer Yard, which had been one of the busiest in Kent, there were a pair of custom built coppers. These were built of brick, the top part and about 2 feet down being cement rendered. Each copper held about 120 gallons and had its own fire grate and flue leading to a common chimney. In front of the coppers was a raised standing

---

*Sere, a word commonly used in North Kent to describe wood that had completely dried out and was likely to snap like a carrot.

Tar coppers at White's Conyer yard.

area of about 3 feet wide and one foot above the floor. This allowed a man to reach into the coppers with a ladle when filling a pail with hot stuff. The building was a wooden frame covered with corrugated iron sheets; it had shutters on three sides to allow the fumes to escape. If any of the locals had a cold, they would come to stand in the fumes which they believed to be a cure. Over the years I worked there, I had many colds but the fumes never cured any of mine in spite of the hours spent in them. Hot stuff was a mixture of coal tar and pitch boiled together. It was not quite as simple as it sounds, mainly because the quality of tar from local gasworks varied so much that it was impossible to work out a proportionate mixture so that

The Hot Stuff pail. Note the wooden stop to keep the handle clear of the Hot Stuff.

each fresh batch had to be examined and tested at regular intervals. Starting from scratch, the copper would be three-parts filled with coal tar then the fire would be lit. A low fire would be sufficient for the first hour but once the tar had warmed through some pitch was added and the fire was increased. From now on the copper would want watching as, when heat increased, it was liable to boil over like milk. If this happened, it would feed the firebox with boiling tar oil with the result that you had a serious fire on your hands. If the tar was seen to be rising, one would shout 'Hot Stuff rising', one of the shipwrights would run up to the coppers and, picking up the long handled ladle, would start to lift the hot stuff and tip it back into the copper. This circulated air into the bubbling oil and allowed it to settle; the copper was never safe until all the tar oil had been boiled off. Once again, more pitch would be added and the foreman would then start his tests by dipping a stick into the copper and allowing it to dry. He would test it by gripping the stick with his thumb and forefinger and the amount of effort needed to part them from the stick told him how much pitch or tar must be added to obtain the right mixture. The tar was delivered from the gas works in 40-gallon steel barrels which were set up on stands high enough to set a pail under the small bung hole. Sometimes the tar was thin and oily which meant trouble for us while at other times, especially in winter, it was so thick that the blacksmith heated an iron rod to push into the bung hole — a primitive immersion heater which would be frowned upon by present day Factory Acts. The pitch was delivered in wooden barrels which had to be broken up to get the pitch out.

15

Preparing to pull a plank out of the steam chest.

During busy times both coppers would be in use; one for the current batch, the other for mixing a new batch so that there was always some ready for use. The fuel for the coppers was, of course, waste edging off planks which one had to saw into lengths of 3 feet with a rusty old handsaw kept especially for the job. As one had to be at work early — six in the morning — to light the coppers, one usually tried to get some wood ready the previous afternoon, it being almost impossible to find any in the darkness of a winter's morning. As a fourteen-year-old boy, I made sure that I had some kindling inside as there was no lighting of any sort and most mornings seemed to be damp with fog or rain and bitter cold winds blowing. I was glad to light the fire under the copper and curl up close to it to get some warmth into my frail young body. When hot stuff was needed it would be shouted for and then one had to stand the pail on top of the copper and, with a long handled ladle, three-parts fill it, remove the mop from the copper where it had been put to soften up, place the mop in the pail and carry the lot into the building shed. This may sound easy but for a young boy it was a considerable weight and the fact that it was at boiling point and was liable to spill down one's leg made one very careful how one carried it. Our coppers did, in fact, catch fire in 1938: they had boiled over within a minute of being left. The building was burnt out completely and the whole lot was rebuilt and in use within a week!

THE STEAM CHEST

The steam chest was anything that could hold a few planks and a lot of steam. If someone was going to build one barge, he would knock up a rough box and have a drum of water with a fire under it; a pipe would lead the steam to the box and he would have a reasonable steam chest. Steam chests would vary from one boat yard to another. An average custom built one would be about 40 to 50 feet long by 3 feet by 2 feet. The one at White's at Conyer was built of pine planks, 12 inches by 2 inches with tongued joints to make it steam tight. It had a door at each end; I will explain why, later. About every 6 feet, it had pieces of 6 inch by 2 inch wood on two facing sides with long bolts through to hold the lot together. Inside, on the bottom of the chest were, at 6 feet intervals, pieces of 4 inch by 2 inch oak; these were to keep the planks off the bottom, allowing the steam to penetrate the maximum area of the planks. The planks were slid into the steam chest on edge with a clear space between them with odd pieces of offcut wood pushed in to keep them apart. Usually, we put four planks at a time in the steam chest, it being uneconomical to steam for less; this could be arranged when building new barges but when repairs were on hand, we have had to steam for just one plank. The planks were marked on the end with chalk to identify them. As there would be one for each quarter of the barge, they would be marked P.F. (port forward), S.F. (starboard forward), P.A. (port aft) and S.A. (starboard aft). Steaming of planks generally took about four hours for planks up to 2 inches thick and an extra hour for every inch over. Of course, the time for steaming timber depended a lot on how long the timber had been seasoned and also different kinds of timber needed different steaming times. I remember being shown how to tell by the amount of sap being driven out of the end grain by the steam penetrating the end of the planks. About every hour, the door would be taken off to see how the steaming was progressing; the door had felt fastened around the edges to make as tight a fit as possible when in the closed position. Steam was provided by a vertical boiler, protected by a wooden shed which had been built round it. In its time, it had been heavily tarred; even the roof was wood with roofing felt. No one would insure us against fire. Under today's safety laws, it would have had to be rebuilt with less combustible materials. The fuel for this boiler was mainly plank edging which had been cut up with an old hand saw; rarely could one keep up with the voracious appetite of this roaring monster who would shake on her foundations if one forgot to feed her with water! Many times I have heard her thumping and looked through the door at the sight glass and seen no water, at which I have turned on the feed cock and retreated to a safer place for at least five minutes. All the shavings, chips, tar and hair went in: if it would burn, it was fuel for the boiler. Tar and hair was ruinous for washday. In fact, I found that first thing in the morning was the time to burn tar and hair. At that time, most people had not yet hung out their washing and the combination of the two

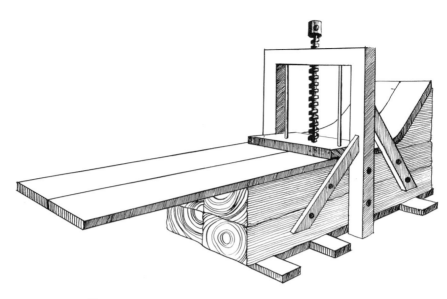

The press for bending swim planks on swim head lighters.

raised steam quickly. No excuses were allowed for poor heads of steam. On one occasion, having great difficulty in getting a head of steam, the blacksmith brought me in two pails full of house coal. I never questioned his source but was grateful to get it on the fire as soon as possible. After about five minutes, the guv'nor came into the boiler shed asking 'Where did you get the coal from?' I was taken aback and did not quite like to tell him. However, I need not have worried as he had guessed. I was still looking a bit puzzled, wondering how he found out when, as if he had read my thoughts, he told me that coal smoke smells different from wood smoke. The coal was his winter stock for his home — I never chanced burning coal again!

Around the inside of the boiler shed were racks on which were stacked trunnels, the warm air helping to season them. On cold days, as many of us as could squeeze in would come into the boiler shed to have our meal breaks. A lot of pushing and shoving went on to get nearest the fire box door to toast one's sandwiches — even jam butties which, after being packed for several hours, had become soggy. Toasting them made them more palatable even to hungry growing lads.

When the planks were ready to bend, the one in charge of the steam chest would take the plank tongs to the door; the tongs were like a massive pair of pincers. At the handle end was a chain leading to a ring which had a long rope tail. Before taking off the door, the boy would ask which plank was wanted. On being told, he would quickly remove the door, take a deep

18

breath and dive into the cloud of very hot steam, find the right plank and grip it with the large tongs. Then he gave a shout to pull and the men would pull out the plank at a run, unhook the tongs, spread themselves out each end of the plank and quickly run into the building shed with it. To save getting their shoulders burnt, they had thick pads of old sacking between the plank and their shoulders; their hands were kept off the plank until they lowered it into its bending position.

I mentioned earlier that the steam chest had a door at each end. The other door was only used when we were building swim head barges. At this end of the steam chest was a large press which was a permanent fixture. It was used for putting short bends in swim planks so that the joint came underneath the bottom instead of right on the bend itself making a much stronger joint. The press had a main body about 12 feet in length made up of baulks to a 30-inch square solid lump of timber. About 30 inches in from one end, two oak posts, about 7 feet long by 8 inches were bolted one each side with a cross bar of the same dimensions strapped to it with thick iron plates and the lot through-bolted together. In the centre of the cross-bar was a threaded boss and a large threaded bar worked through it very much like a cider press. On the bottom of this bar was a shaped wooden former which pressed the steamed planks onto another former fixed to the main body of the press. The press was so positioned that the planks could be drawn out of the steam chest straight onto the press body. After pressing, they would be left in the press overnight to cool off so as to maintain their shape.

THE TOOLS

I was once in company with the late Jack Harris, an older shipwright of Conyer, who finished up at the Sittingbourne Shipbuilding Company. We got to talking about the old days at Conyer Barge Yard. In his time there, one or two of the shipwrights liked their beer and had been known to go on a bender for a day or two, or as long as their money lasted. When their money was all spent, they would then start to sell their tools leaving their saw, adze and maul to the last. This led our conversation to how many tools a shipwright really needed to carry out his work. We came to the conclusion that it was very few for a journeyman shipwright — in fact, he could carry them in his toolbag over his shoulder with the maul helve passed through the handles of the toolbag. This is something I have done myself many times when I have been sent along a sea wall to meet a sailing barge which needed some attention too small to warrant going on the yard.

A shipwright usually had his tool chest which was left at his place of employment. His basic tools were: adze, maul, ripsaw and perhaps a No.6 saw, a jack plane and smoothing plane, plough plane, rebate plane, spokeshave, drawknife, set of firmer chisels, a few socket chisels, a few gouges, scribers, hammer, pricker, rule, square, bevel, brace and bits of various sizes, and perhaps a chalk line and cold chisel. Anything beyond these was

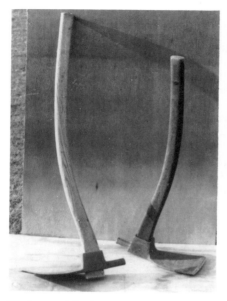

The long and the short handled adzes used by shipwrights. (Douglas Spooner)

The shipwrights maul. (Douglas Spooner)

Planes used in the bargeyard. (Douglas Spooner)

supplied by the yard. Some shipwrights preferred their own trunnel augers and caulking mallet and irons. Caulking was, in fact, a separate trade and caulkers used to travel from job to job and usually worked at piecework rates.

The tools supplied by the barge yard were usually the heavy sort that could not be carried easily such as the large G cramps and long cramps, large augers and trunnel boring machines, trunnel moot, large nail punches, plumb bobs and levels. There were others such as nipcrows — used for removing bent nails — and bolt engines for removing bolts. In the saw pits there were perhaps a few saws but usually the pit sawyer had his own saws, as did my uncle which, on leaving, he left there as pit sawing was rapidly coming to an end as a permanent job. The mechanical saw was taking over the work of converting trees into planks; only the knees and shaped frames being still cut over the pit.

The Shipwright's Adze: The adze is not an easy tool to use but once one has mastered it a more useful tool cannot be found. Surplus wood which would take hours to plane off can be removed in minutes, leaving a surface that needs only the minimum of planing to obtain a smooth surface. It is made in four sizes of which the largest, a No. 4, is the size most used, being about 6 to 7 inches wide at the cutting edge when new and about 9 inches long in the blade. It has a peg at one end used for driving in spikes below the surface of the wood which is to be adzed. The handle or haft is shaped for balance. Some have a double curve, others have a single curve — it is a matter of personal choice which one suits you. Personally, I like the single curved haft; in fact, I was the only one at the yard to use this type, the others preferred the double curved haft. The size is usually stamped on the inside of the blade. Another type of adze used was the strap adze which was only 2 inches wide; this was used for cutting out scarphs. The shipwright's adze had a curved blade while the carpenter's adze was much flatter.

The Maul: To my way of thinking, this was the most perfectly balanced of all the hammers, with a round face at one end tapering off to about ½ inch at the other end. The haft was about 2 feet 10 inches long; some I have seen longer. It was about 6 to 8 lbs in weight. They varied from place to place. In fact, we had some special mauls for driving trunnels. These had a soft face and were no good for driving spikes or bolts.

Saws: Saws in use were ripsaws with either four and a half or five teeth to the inch, used for ripping with the grain. A six tooth to the inch saw was used for cutting across the grain. The ripsaw was sharpened almost square to the blade while the crosscut was sharpened at an angle.

Planes: Perhaps the most important plane was the jack plane which was used for straightening the edges of planks. For the finer work, a tryplane would be used because, owing to its extra length, it would level out the edges

One of the many uses for the drawknife.   (P. O'Driscoll)

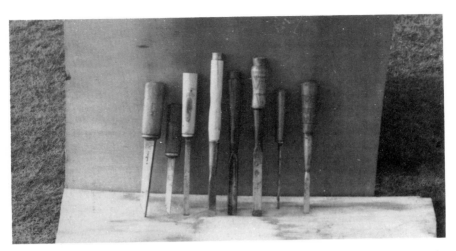

Heavy chisels used by bargebuilders.   (Douglas Spooner)

much straighter. The smoothing plane was for general work and would almost certainly be used to remove adze marks. Rebate planes were used for planing out rebates in plank edges. These came in various sizes and shapes, many being made for special jobs with a curved bottom for hollowing. Plough planes were used for ploughing out grooves of various widths and usually had about ten or so different width irons (blades). These irons could be bought separately or made in the blacksmith's shop. The spokeshave could be called a plane with two handles and was used for smoothing off round corners or hollows where a plane could not be used.

The Drawknife: This was not essentially a shipwright's tool but was much used for removing surplus wood such as chamfering edges of beams and, in the right hands, was a very useful tool. I recall my tutor telling me of a shipwright who did most of his shaping with his tool because he was short of other tools.

Chisels: With the heavy work involved in barge building, heavy tools were necessary. The lightest chisels used were the firmer chisels; the ones without the bevelled edge. Much heavier chisels were needed such as mortice chisels and socket chisels. The socket chisel had a taper socket into which fitted a wooden handle. This allowed it to be hit a lot harder than the firmer chisel as the handle could be replaced quite easily. There were, in fact, some barge builders' chisels which had steel handles but I have never seen any of these. The largest of the socket chisels we called pinching chisels; by inserting the tip under a shore, one could lift tremendous weights with them.

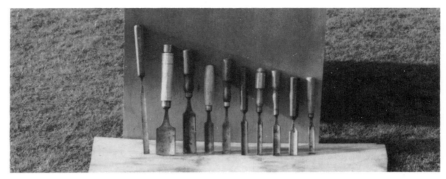

Gouges used by bargebuilders. (Douglas Spooner)

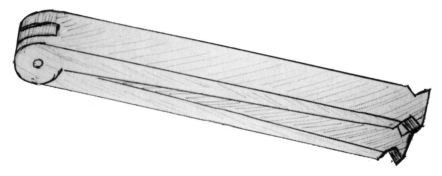

Shipwright's scribers.

Bevels mostly used in bargeyards. (Douglas Spooner)

Gouges: Bargebuilders' gouges were also socketed for heavy use but most men had a collection of carpenters' gouges as well. These came in two different types — those sharpened on the inside and others sharpened on the outside. Gouges were used mostly for carving and countersinking bolt heads, etc.

Scribers: Barge builders' scribers seem to be a bit of mystery to the layman. I have never seen them mentioned or illustrated although they were a most important item of a barge builder's tool kit. Hinged at one end like a divider, they were flat on both legs and at the ends of the legs a V section was filed on both sides of each leg. When fitting a plank to another plank, the scribers would be opened to the widest gap. They would then be drawn along, marking the shape of one plank onto the other plank, the mark would then be planned out and a perfect fit obtained.

Pricker: This was a longish piece of steel tapered to a point. When fitting timber heads to floors, a dovetail joint would be used or sometimes a half dovetail. A hole would be bored through the female dovetail in the floor, the timber head with the male dovetail would be tapped into place, the pricker would then be inserted into the holes in the floor and pricked around onto the timber head. This would mark the position of the hole onto the timber head. To ensure the two went together tight, the hole in the timber head would be bored slightly up and outboard of the prick marks, ensuring the timber head was drawn down thus making a tight fit of the joint.

Rule: A 2-foot folding rule was standard at the Conyer Yard although it was up to each man what he used. A 100-foot tape was supplied when needed.

Square: It was best to have a selection of squares of different sizes.

Bevels: Most men would have at least three bevels — a large wooden one made out of hardwood with a thumbscrew to tighten it up after being set, a metal adjustable one and a double-ended one, one end with a 3-inch blade, the other end being 6 inches.

Brace and Bits: These were standard rachet braces as were the bits.

Chalkline: About 60 feet of cotton line on a wooden reel, used for lining out planks and logs as a guideline when sawing.

Cold Chisel: Used for the cutting of bolts, etc.

Shipwright's Axe: Used for a number of different jobs, usually where the adze could not be used.

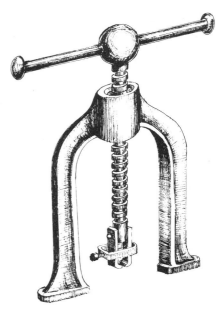

A shipwright's axe.   (Douglas Spooner)

Bolt engine

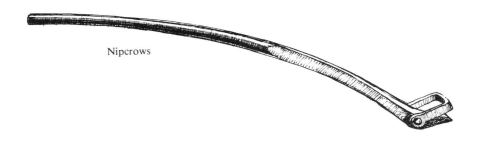

Standard and short swing brace.

Nipcrows

26

TOOLS USUALLY SUPPLIED BY THE YARD

Too heavy to be carried around by a journeyman shipwright were the large cramps and long ship cramps. The G cramps varied in size; some were so large one man could just about lift them into position and wind the handle. When steaming a plank, a G cramp would be used on every timber head or frame so that the plank was pulled in tight to the shape of the barge. The building of one barge would require about twenty-four G cramps if four planks were steamed at one time. The ship cramps were used for cramping the bottom together. When all the bottom had been laid, these would be replaced with long iron bars threaded at each end, one bar over the top and one underneath. At each end a steel plate with two holes would be slipped over the bars and a nut put on the threaded ends. The nuts would then be tightened up allowing the cramps to be used for other purposes.

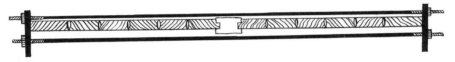

Bottom planks were cramped together with long bolts and plates.

Nipcrows: As they were called at the Conyer Yard, were like a large crow bar. At the bottom end, there was a U shaped piece of iron spanning the width of the bar. This had a rivet through it and the bar, so that the U shape was movable and could be hooked over the spike head. The end of the bar rested against the spike so that when one pressed down on the handle it pinched the spike against the U piece and allowed it to be drawn out. So much pressure could be exerted that it was quite common to snap off 7-inch spikes.

Bolt Engine: Made of steel, probably in the blacksmith's shop. They were U shaped with a foot on each leg, the legs being about 2 feet long. At the top was a central boss threaded to take a 1-inch threaded bar. The threaded bar had at its bottom end two claws over which slipped a retaining clip with a set bolt in one end. The claws were slipped over the head of the bolt, the clip slipped over the claws and the set screw tightened up. Then the threaded bar would be turned with the slide through handle which would in turn draw out the bolt.

Trunnel Hole Borer: One could either sit or kneel on these. Both ways were painful. There were two handles like bicycle pedals which you turned with your hands and it was fitted with a 1⅛ inch bit. It was not long before arms began to ache; after a time when the arms could no longer take it, you picked up a pod auger and did it the hard way.

The trunnel hole boring machine.   (Author)

The trunnel mute used for rounding up trunnels which came to the yard as eight-sided chopped
out oak pegs.   (P. O'Driscoll)

Trunnel Moot: Another steel tool, very heavy but easy to use, usually set at 1⅛ inches to turn the eight sided trunnels into a round shape. There are some made of hardwood; these can only do one size whereas the steel ones are adjustable.

Pit Saws: Usually were supplied in the yard but some journeymen sawyers preferred their own. The saws varied in size; for sawing a 5-foot diameter tree, a 9-foot saw would be used; there were two of them at the Conyer Yard. Shorter saws would be used for lighter timber. For sawing round curves, a narrow bladed saw of about 5 feet in length was used. There would be handspikes and dog irons kept at the pit for moving and fixing round timber.

THE HALF MODEL

Almost all barges were built from half models, either the solid type or one of station and battens. The *Sara*, built at Conyer, was built from a station and batten model. This model was at Conyer until George Gates, the manager, died, when Arthur White collected it and took it to London. All the rest of the models in our loft were solid, carved from yellow pine; some of these were sandwich or lift built. I have seen lines taken off half models by various methods, all of which seem to have the same result. It did not seem to matter if stations were out by the odd ½ inch as, once framed up and the fairing batten placed round, the adze would soon take off the high spots and a bit more trimming was always done when fitting the planks; it was most important that the planks lay flat to the timber heads for maximum strength. Most sailing barges were built from the solid model, the position of the frames and timber heads being marked on the half model in pencil. We must assume that the model was made to a scale. Therefore, before we start to take off the lines, our paper must be squared to the same scale. We are now ready to start. Taking a piece of strip lead, we start at the first frame marked on the half model and bend the lead to shape along the pencil mark. If working from the bow, we use the after side of the marked frame which will be the widest position from the centre line. After bending the lead, we lay it onto our squared paper and carefully mark round the inside edge. We carry on doing this till all frames with shape up to the straight timber heads are done. We then move aft and do the same except that we take them from the forward side of the frames which again is the widest position from the centre line. The bevel will be allowed for when marking out full size onto the timber.

The lift model was seldom used as the method was a bit more complicated though more accurate but, as I have already said, accuracy was not so essential in a sailing barge as it would be in a ship. The lift model was made up of boards to a scale thickness placed one on top of the other, each one being screwed to the one underneath. When enough had been screwed together,

Sawyers cutting a log into planks.

The pit saw, one of many at the Conyer yard of Whites.   (The late Mrs F. Austin)

the model was shaped. When taken to pieces, the distances from the centre line could be taken at each stage and marked onto the squared paper with dots. When all positions were marked, the dots could be joined up with curved lines to the shape of each frame. I have heard it said that some builders cut their solid models through square to the centre line and marked around the cut off sections onto their squared paper. This may be why some yards never seemed to have any half models left in their lofts.

THE SAW PIT
Over the centuries, many methods have been devised for the converting of logs into usable timber. Drawings on walls of very ancient buildings, paintings and many of the old books had such drawings illustrated in them. We see old pictures of logs leaning on walls being sawn downwards by a man with a handsaw, others showing the use of two trestles, one always appearing much higher than the other, the log resting on top being a precarious looking set up which could be dangerous to both the top and bottom sawyers. Most barge yards had their own saw pits which were dug into the ground. The early ones were boarded up inside to stop them collapsing, later they were bricked up and rendered with a cement sand facing to try to stop the ingress of water. At Conyer, we had two pits side by side; one about 18 feet long and the other about 14 feet long. They were about 5 feet wide and a little over 6 feet deep. The top had a wooden surround of timber baulks about 16 by 8 inches, firmly fixed into masonry with bolts — a very strong arrangement but necessary to accommodate the large oaks and elms that were sawn into timber and planks.

Across the pits, eight-sided wooden rollers were placed and the tree positioned on top of the rollers. When the tree was in place, one end of an iron dog was driven into the tree, the other end into the wooden cill surrounding the pit. This was to stop the tree rolling during the sawing; the rollers were also dogged to prevent any chance of the tree moving along the pit. The 8-sided rollers were found to be more controllable than round ones when moving the tree along the pit. The rollers were about 9 inches in diameter and had holes bored through the ends where a steel bar could be inserted to move the tree short distances if the need arose. Normally a wire cable was led through snatch blocks to pull the tree into position and hand spikes were used to line up the tree with the pit. Only one winch was used at the Conyer Yard. This served all the sheds as well as the saw pit by leading the cable through a series of snatch blocks. Little complicated equipment was needed in a sawpit — a collection of saws of various lengths, handspikes, axes, chalk line and chalk, a large pair of dividers, maul and wedges, saw sharpening horse and files. Most times there was a timber jack, race knife and, inside the pit, a pot of waste oil and a brush (to oil the saw) and the saw's box (the saw's bottom handle which fastened on the bottom of the saw by various means) and, of course, a broom and shovel to clean out the saw pit. The different kinds of sawdust were kept separate; the oak was sold for various usages and the pine was sold to butcher's shops to spread on the floors. Other sawdust was sold to local farmers to spread on the floors of their poultry houses.

The sawyer, after setting up his tree over the pit, would then have to decide what size saw to use, depending on the diameter of the tree. On a large oak, he would need a 9-foot saw which he would use for the first half of the tree then, as the size diminished, he would take a shorter saw, otherwise the poor pit man would be working on his knees.

If the tree was to be sawn into planks he would mark the tree with his chalk line, plumbing the lines down the end of the tree after which he would saw down all of the lines to the first roller. The first roller would then be shifted forward along the sawn part until there was sufficient room to get the saw back into the sawcuts, when he would continue to saw the tree as far as the next roller. That roller would then be moved forward. This process would be repeated until the tree was all cut up into planks which were taken outside and stacked one on top of the other as they were sawn. Battens of wood about ½ inch thick would be placed in between at about 4-foot intervals to allow air to circulate and so season the timber.

Not all the timber that was sawn over the pit was in tree form. Imported softwoods such as pines were squared in the forests to save space on board the ships which carried them to this country. Many of these baulks were used at Conyer in the old days when a gang of men would leave Conyer in a rowing boat and row out to the Medway or Sheerness depending on where the ship was bound. The baulks would be thrown overboard and made up into a raft by nailing rope across and leading it underneath to bind them all together. The men would have taken an anchor with them in the boat and several setting booms which were used to push the raft along. The boat would have been pulled up onto the raft for the journey home.

Once the tide turned against them, they would anchor the raft, put the boat into the water and row ashore to make their way home as best they could, returning to catch the next tide. I was told by Rob Gates that he helped to fetch a raft from Queenborough once and they were fortunate in catching the tide right and made the mouth of Conyer Creek before they had to anchor.

At the creek end of the sawpit there was a timber-lined slipway which was used to get the baulk out of the water and onto the sawpit, the rear end of the sawpit shed being removable for this purpose.

The sharpening of the saw was important. What was a good sharp and set for oak would probably be hard work trying to cut a pine baulk, but the method of sharpening could only be arrived at by years of experience. In fact, two baulks of pine may not cut the same but the sawyer would know what alteration was needed to his saw.

Chapter II:

Building A Barge

RAISING THE STOCKS

The stocks where a barge was built was a removable base on which the bottom was laid. The sheds at Conyer had a fall of 6 feet in 90 which was maintained when raising the stocks. Even a barge constructed in the open needed a beach which sloped down to the water to make launching easy. On occasion, barges have been built inland and moved over slipways to the water, but this is obviously not economically viable when better sites are readily available.

Once the dimensions of the barge were known, the position of the stocks could be marked out with small pegs and a centre line put through the site for squaring off and setting up. The stocks consisted of a deal (plank) about 9 inches by 3 inches. This was then blocked up at each end until it was about 30 inches above the ground, making sure the deal was level. When correctly in position, stumps would be driven into the ground and nailed to the deal to prevent it from moving, more blocks would then be placed under the centre of the deal. Using a line between the two end stocks which were erected first, the others could easily be filled in at roughly 8-foot intervals. Then two more blocks were placed, one at each end, to take the stem and stern posts.

Depending on the type of bottom laid, as for example with the Lee Conservancy barges which were built at Conyer, it was sometimes necessary to cut a slot along the axis of the stocks for a keel to sit in if it was to protrude beyond the bottom planking.

LAYING THE BOTTOM

There are at least three different ways of laying a barge's bottom. They are: the plain dowelled joint; the rebated joint and the double planked method, all of which were used at various times. None ever proved itself better than the other although some old barge builders had their own favoured way.

The first plank to be laid is the keel plank, usually of elm and almost always in three pieces, scarphed at the joints with felt and hotstuff between the scarph before fastening. The keel plank varied with the size of the barge: an average sized keel would be about 14 inches by 5 inches and would

Showing the stocks on which a barge was built. This one was a canal barge, although the method was the same as a sailing barge. Note: tar and hair joints.   (The late Stewart Dixon)

increase in thickness at each end to about 7 inches where the stem and stern posts would be fitted to it with an oak knee through-bolted at the keel and posts. Working from the keel outwards, Oregon pine planks would be fitted up to the chine plank which would be of elm; elm being a very good wood for taking fastenings such as the rose-headed spikes which would be driven into it when the sides were planked up. The bottom planks would be planed with a jack plane to get a reasonably straight edge after which a plane with a convex bottom was used on each edge to hollow it out about ⅛ inch deep. A plank each side of the keel would be fitted and a hand saw would next be run down each joint to make sure the joint fitted. This would continue until the whole of the bottom was laid. Once the bottom was in position and temporarily cramped up, the floor positions could be marked across the bottom, usually about 20-inch centres, after which the bottom could be taken up once again and the dowel holes marked and bored between the floor markings. This made sure that when boring trunnel holes later, through the floors and bottom planks, the bit of the boring tool did not hit a dowel. The bottom was now ready for stuffing. A plank each side of the keel would be stood on edge by means of a long-handled mop after which a layer of elk or cow hair would be applied to the prepared edge. The hot stuff would then be applied to the layer of hair and the plank lowered down and cramped into position. This would go on until all the planks were in place, the cramps would then be taken off and replaced by two long bars threaded at each end with plates slipped over the bar ends and nuts put onto the threaded ends which would be tightened with a long-handled spanner every hour for two days. It was then left to settle for a day or two before the floors were laid. Some yards used chain halters around the bottom and drove wedges in at each side to tighten joints.

Working from a centre line which had been put on the keel, the width of the bottom was next marked on the chine plank. This was sawn and adzed to shape then trued up with a jack plane. When this was finished the floor could be laid. Having laid all the floors on the bottom, the ends were marked for length and the limbers marked in their positions after which the floors could be taken up and the ends cut off and a half dovetail or dovetail cut in ready to receive the timber heads. Limber holes would then be cut in the under sides of the floors. These were slots cut across the width of the floors on the bottom side to allow the water to flow to the pumps which were positioned one each side both fore and aft so that whatever the angle of heel the barge had the water would flow to one or the other of the pumps.

The slots were usually about 2 to 2½ inches wide by 1 inch deep, positioned where no spikes or treenails would foul them. Before the floors were lifted, their position would have been marked across the bottom. Holes would be bored for the spikes to be driven upwards before putting the floors back. A G cramp would be put on each end of the floor to hold it in position and the spike driven through. Once the floors were all spiked, an apprentice would be given the job of boring the trunnel holes, first with a boring machine pedalled with the hands then a pod auger would be run through to make sure the hole was true. This was a back-breaking job and raised blisters on the hands. About forty holes in each floor made it a never-ending job. It was a spare time job which meant that it was done when there was nothing more important to do.

FRAMING UP

Now that the floors were fastened to the bottom, framing up could commence. A timber head would be set up at each quarter at the station where the straight sides finish and the 'runs' commence. The timber head would be squared with the bottom and a plumbob used to get the right amount of fall off (outward angle from the upright). When these four timber heads had been fitted and fastened, temporary bracing straps of plank edging would be fastened from the timber head to the floor and across the top from one timber head to the other.

The depth of the barge side was marked on the timber heads (this would be to the under side of the deck), a harpin would then be fixed outside the timber heads on each side — the harpin would be about 3 inches by 2½ inches of pine. The one at Conyer was laminated boards which gave it

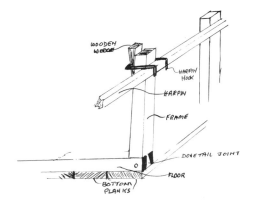

WOODEN WEDGE

HARPIN HOOK

HARPIN

FRAME

DOVETAIL JOINT

FLOOR

BOTTOM PLANKS

Take over joint clearly displayed here.

greater strength. The timber head at the nearest station to the middle would be the next one fitted, it being made easier now the harpin was in position. The square mark could be marked on the harpin, the timber head stood against it, a harpin hook dropped over the lot and a wedge was tapped in. It was then held tightly in position to mark the half dovetail joint on the bottom of the timber head.

By the time the straight timbers had been fitted, the patterns for the forward frames would have been made up of rough board and taken to the sawyer who would have marked them on the flitches, taking advantage of the differing shapes to get as many as possible out of his flitches without waste. These would be fitted in position against a curved harpin made up specially for each barge, as no two barges were the same shape. When all the frames had been fitted, some of which were cant frames, fairing battens would be fixed round and the timber heads and frames would be faired off with the adze and plane so that when the planks were fitted they would lie evenly against all the frames and timber heads.

Before taking the harpin away, the frames and timber heads would be braced to prevent them moving when the outside planking was fitted. After everything was braced, the harpin could be taken away and a sheer batten, held in place by batten hooks, would be spied in by eye, perhaps being shifted a dozen times before it satisfied the foreman shipwrights who took great pride in the looks of their barges. Building a barge for the up-river trade could not have given them much pleasure, knowing that she was going to be almost flat to enable her to go under the low bridges and through tunnels. Perhaps they were rewarded otherwise as some of these low flat barges were very fast and made some extraordinary passages to London from the Swale via the Ham Gat outside the Isle of Sheppey and the same

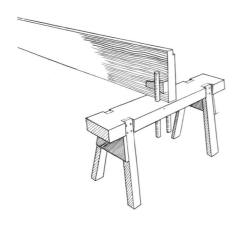

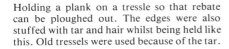

Holding a plank on a tressle so that rebate can be ploughed out. The edges were also stuffed with tar and hair whilst being held like this. Old tressels were used because of the tar.

The method of fixing staging around a barge.

way back. I sailed on one of these as mate in 1936 and found it to be very wet in a choppy sea, almost every wave coming aboard and rolling along where the deck should have been and washing the feet of the man at the wheel. Of course, these brick barges were loaded down to within 2 inches of the deck when they left the Swale which is salt water. Once you get up-river, you lose the buoyancy as the water gets fresher and suddenly you find your decks almost covered by water.

PLANKING UP

The first plank to be fitted on the outside would be the outwhale. Already, the sheerline would have been marked in so that the top edge of the outwhale could be fitted to this mark. The plank may have been cut to shape or steamed and bent on edge by fixing the ends and cramping the middle down to the sheerline mark. Outwhales were thicker than the rest of the skin planks except the chine planks; it was a matter of putting the strength where it was needed. So many fastenings went into the outwhale, especially the fastenings of the covering boards which had to be the best possible — a plain joint which had to be watertight. This joint also has a lot of stress when the barge twists in a seaway. I have seen covering boards open and shut when sailing in a stiff breeze. This usually happened when the barge was getting old, but a lot depended on how the barge had been treated or how many bad berths she had been sat in during her very hard lifetime.

37

Bending run planks

Whaleplanks were always of oak, chineplanks of elm and, if the rest of the skin was to be pitch pine, it would be put on in two layers with barge felt in between the layers, the joints being 'set work' with hot stuff and hair. If the planking was to be oak, it would be a single thickness with rebated joints set in hot stuff and hair. The thickness of the planking depended on the size of the barge being built; a river barge would have 2 to 2½ inches whereas a coasting barge would be 3 to 3½ inches, the whales and chines being about one inch thicker.

When planking up with oak planks, the edges would be rebated. The rebate would be made by ploughing a groove along the edge of the plank so that half the thickness would be removed, then ploughing another groove in the face of the plank to meet the bottom of the groove ploughed in the edge. A strip of wood is then removed from the corner. This was a useful batten which we used for placing in between planks to allow a flow of air for seasoning. Only the edge to be fitted would be completely rebated; the other edge would be ploughed out but not so deeply, leaving the rebate batten still affixed to the plank. There was a reason for this. When fitting planks, cramps are used on the edge of the planks. If the rebate is taken out, a piece of wood would have to be put into the rebate to prevent the edge of the plank being damaged. By leaving the partly ploughed out rebate in position, cramps can be used without the need for finding a piece of wood for the rebate. Later, when the plank has been fitted and fastened, the rebate can be cut out with a chisel. We found this was best done with a sash pocket chisel which is not a shipwright's tool but is perfect for the job. If pitch pine or other pines were to be used for planking up in two layers, the joints of the outer layer would be staggered to form a rebate. This made it necessary to work out beforehand where the outside joints were to be to look right; the inside joints could then be arranged accordingly.

BENDING THE RUN PLANKS

Now that the barge is framed up we can start to finish the bottom planking; that is the planking that starts at the end of the flat bottom and curves its way to either the stem post or the transom. At the end of the flat bottom, the planks would have been halved at the nearest floor, ready to receive the first run plank which will be of elm. First, a batten will be placed along and fastened with batten hooks. The batten will then be bent round the timber heads and frames without forcing it, letting it take its natural way. Measurements would be taken from the keel plank to one edge of the batten and then pencilled onto the batten at the spot where they were taken. The width of the plank at the stem end would have to be worked out in width according to how many planks there were to be fastened to the stem; the same procedure was applied to the stern planking. This was called 'taking the go' of a plank. When all the measurements were marked on the batten, it would be taken to the plank stack and the stack would be turned down until a suitable plank was found which had as little waste as possible. The plank would then be marked out from the batten, lined out with a chalk line and taken to the pit to be cut to shape. When all four planks — one for each quarter — had been cut, they would be ready for steaming and would be placed in the steam chest. Once steamed, they would be carried into the shed. The end which was to join the bottom would be placed over the lap and cramped in position then, with the bender, the plank would be gradually bent and twisted. At each frame, a pair of G cramps would be hooked on and tightened; if it was too awkward to cramp, a shore would be used with ship wedges driven in until the plank was in tight to the frames.

The planks would be left to cool off for a day then taken off and fitted. The half lap was cut in where it joined the bottom and the stem end fitted into the rebate. Along the keel, the plank would be shaped to the angle required to fit into the keel rebate. Finally, before taking the plank off to be stuffed, a trunnel hole would be bored; this was called a pitching trunnel. The nail holes also would be marked and then bored when on the trestles ready for stuffing. Before stuffing, a trunnel with a tipped end would be driven into the plank so that it projected through about 1 inch. After stuffing, this trunnel was entered into the hole in the frame and driven in with a maul; this made sure that the plank was positioned properly before applying the G cramps which were screwed up quickly and tightly. When all the cramps were on and tight, the spikes were driven and then the cramps could be removed. There was usually a man and a boy working each quarter but when a plank had been stuffed, the man would shout 'Pitch up wanted' and more men would come to help to pitch the plank until all the cramps were on.

All the run planks would be fitted until level with the chine planks by which time all the planks with twists and shape would be fitted. The rest would only need bending, with perhaps a bit of curve round the transom which was never much of a problem.

BEAMS, KNEES AND KEELSONS

As soon as the barge was framed up and the 'planking up' under way, some of the shipwrights would be fitting the beams, knees and breasthook together with the deck carlings. These all added strength to the structure of the barge and, of course, gave work to the blacksmith, making bolts to fasten the knees to the beams and timber heads. Before the beams or carlings could be fitted, an inwale had to be put around the inside which, depending on how big a barge it was, could be anything up to 15 by 4 inch English oak. Bolted to the frames, it formed a shelf for the ends of the beams and carlings to rest on. Sometimes the beams were joggled into it for added strength. The beams would be fitted with large wooden knees to the frames. The horizontal ones were called lodge knees and the ones set vertically called haning knees. Later barges used iron knees which took up less space, were much stronger and did not rot like so many of the wooden ones if the deck leaked. A space about 2 to 3 inches wide was left between the inwale and the next plank down to allow the air to circulate between the frames. Fillet pieces of planking were fitted into these spaces when carrying loose cargoes such as grain, coal, stone etc. Pat O'Driscoll has told me what a job it was to get them out if they had been in for some length of time and therefore swollen until they were tight.

The fitting of beams was fairly simple; just a matter of cutting the ends to fit. The amount of uprise having been decided, it would be marked onto the timber and cut to shape by the sawyer. The centre would be marked and, when fitting the beam, the mark must be in the centre of the barge.

When fitting the knees, a pattern would be made up and taken to the sawyer who would cut it to shape. Two nails would be driven into the beam far enough to support the weight of the knee and one nail into the inwale. The knee would be placed on these nails and a pair of scribers opened to the widest gap. The knees would then be scribed in on both top and bottom sides. Then the knee would be cramped to something solid and adzed to the scribe marks, the edges to be fitted would be hollowed out about an ⅛ inch before being taken back and rested on the nails. It would then have a hand-saw cut run down each leg of the knees to ensure a good fit. The reason for hollowing the edges out was to lessen the task when running the saw along the edges.

Chine keelsons would be fitted on the inside of the frames where they joined the floors. Owing to the shape of the barge, the keelson had to be forced into place with shores. Once in place, it had to be fitted flat against the frames. These were at an angle to the bottom which meant that the bottom edge had to be fitted over each floor separately. Every floor was marked to the widest gap shown, ensuring a fit at every floor once the marks had been sawn and chiseled out. When all the fitting had been finished, the keelson would be shored back into position to be bored and bolted through frames and floors. The holes were bored tight and the pilot pointed bolts driven from the outside. Once all the bolts had been driven, a washer would be put over the bolt and hit with a hammer to mark the wood, the mark would then be cut in with a gouge a little deeper than the thickness of the washer. Next, the washer would be put back on the bolt and the boy would hold a maul against one side of the bolt while the shipwright would make a cut into the bolt with a cold chisel. Changing position, the other side would be cut; the cuts being made about ⅜ inch above the washer. A sharp tap with a hammer would break off the surplus bolt which would then be cold riveted over the washer.

MASTS AND SPARS

At the larger, more established barge yards, a spar shop or shed would be used for the sole purpose of making spars and masts, but the proportion of spars made under these conditions was very small. A rough estimate would be about 15 per cent; the rest would be made up in sheds where the barges were built or outside, weather permitting.

Some yards had enough work to employ a resident spar maker who would be responsible for making masts, booms, sprits, setting booms, oars, hitchers and, if the barge was a coaster, bowsprits and perhaps a yard for the squaresail — which some barges carried — and a headstick if it was a topsail barge.

A barge's mainmast was usually made from a grown pitch pine tree, average length 46 to 50 feet. This would probably arrive into this country in a crude squared baulk to save shipping space. I have seen them arrive in their original tree form which would still have to be squared up before one could start work shaping it. First, the end which was to fit in the mast case would be squared up on all four sides to a point, a little over the top of the mast case, where it would begin to take on its round appearance. It would be a loose fit in the mast case to allow the rigger to set the mast upright.

From the top of the mast case onwards the mast would have been eight-sided, the first step in the rounding-up process. This would have been chopped out with an adze and finished with a jack plane. After this, it would be sixteen-sided, using a drawknife and jack plane, to be followed by

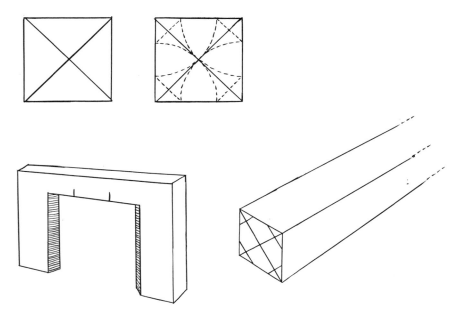

The method of eight siding a square baulk of timber.

planing off all the corners then finishing with a hollow spar plane, scraper and sandpaper.

The foot of the mast would be rounded to suit the dish in the bottom of the mast case. This was to make it easier when hauling up the gear and to keep the right tension on the shrouds and avoid stretching, as would be the case if a sharp corner was left on the bottom of the mast.

Iron work could now be fitted. Starting at the foot, which had been rounded, an iron plate would be fitted to take the wear when the mast was lowered and raised. This was usually of ½ inch plate, bent to shape by the blacksmith, and drilled to take the large clout nails with which it was fastened. On the after side of the mast was the jackstay, an iron bar of ¾ inch diameter which passed through eyebolts driven into the mast. There were six or seven of these eyebolts to the length of the jackstay. The eyebolts had a square tapered shank which was jagged on all corners to resist being pulled out. To fit them, a hole, about the size of the small end of the taper, was bored and then morticed out with a chisel, tapering like the eyebolt but only about half the size. It was chiseled out square to stop the eyebolts from turning when driven. The eyebolts were driven very tight and, as the work progressed, the bar would be threaded through to make sure all of the eyebolts were in line.

42

The jackstay was there to fix the mainsail to, using long shackles; the earlier barges had hoops around the mast for the same purpose.

LAUNCHING

Preparing for a launch came gradually. First, the bottom had to be cleaned off, for tar and hair still hung down from every joint. This was done by going underneath, laying on one's back and pushing a very sharp 2-inch wood chisel — frequently dipped in an oil pot to keep the tar from sticking to the chisel. In a very short time, one's clothes began to stick to one's body. Every so often, one had to get out from underneath and, with a long-handled rake, drag the tar and hair to the outside and wheel it away to be burnt — usually on the boiler. The oil pot would have a quantity of cow hair soaked in oil in it to prevent the loss of oil if the pot was knocked over. The stocks would be dismantled at the same time. The barge would be sitting on four blocks, one at each quarter at the beginning of the runs — where the barge starts to curve in at each end and the bottom starts to rise towards the stern and stem posts.

Different yards had their own method of launching. At Conyer, the bigger barges had double slips, one being placed under each chine and strapped together to stop them spreading. The smaller river barges were launched on a single slip placed under the middle of the barge; as this was only one foot wide, balance was essential. The slips were set up with a convex curve. Years of experience had taught the old shipwrights that dead flat slipways had a tendency to stick after the barge had travelled a short distance, regardless of how much grease had been put on the slips before putting the runners in.

The day before the launch, large bottle jacks would be placed under the stern section and the barge lifted up enough to take the blocks out. The stern would then be lowered onto the slip runner. Temporary blocks would then be put under the stern and wedges driven in tight but not tight enough to lift the barge off the slip runner. Next, the jacks would be taken forward, the blocks taken out and the barge lowered onto the slip runner. Blocks and wedges would then be placed under the chines and the jacks taken away.

Now all the barge was resting on the slip, one could see where the slip needed packing up so that all of it was tight to the bottom. When this had been attended to, it was a matter of waiting for the tide. The end of the shed would have been taken out and ropes attached to check the barge once it was afloat.

Once the tide had risen enough to cover the end of the slipway outside the shed to a depth of 3 feet, it would be time to launch. The only thing holding the barge were the two forward blocks and wedges, the after blocks having been removed. One shipwright would station himself at the port side blocks and another at the starboard side blocks and wait for the foreman's signal. Once the signal was given, they would knock out the wedges with their mauls and the barge would now be free to go. No two barges ever went away the same; some would go with a rush, some would need some help to start them but, once started, they usually kept going. As soon as they were afloat, a rope would be placed under the barge to sweep the slip runners out. Once the runners were out, the barge was moored to the wharf where she was to be fitted out.

The after cabin was fitted out to the owner's specifications. Some of the larger barges had very fine cabins fitted out in mahogany, others in pitch pine. Most of the brick barges were fitted out in deal or fir and were grained and varnished.

The fore cabin was very sparse as all the gear used in running the barge was housed here, although some had bunks fitted (which were seldom used).

THE BLACKSMITH SHOP

The smaller barge yards farmed-out the ironwork to the local smithy. The larger, more established yards, however, had their own blacksmith's shop and were well equipped to handle all the ironwork needed on a barge.

The blacksmith's shop at White's Conyer Yard was about 25 feet by 18 feet. The side facing south had a large window, three parts the length of the wall. It had three large opening sections, top-hung with a long adjustable bar at the bottom having holes 3 inches apart which hooked over a peg in the cill. At one end centrally was the hearth, brick-built about 5 feet square while, at the opposite end to the chimney, there were two cast iron troughs built into the brickwork; the one nearest the chimney was for coal, the adjoining one was for water. Along the edge of the water trough was an iron bar over which were hooked the collection of various shaped tongs needed to handle hot iron while being shaped. The water in the trough was used for wetting the coal dust before putting it on the fire and for cooling hot iron and tempering steel tools such as cold chisels, punches and other tools that had to be made in the smithy for special jobs.

At the end, on one side of the hearth stood a large, pear-shaped bellows operated by a long handle which passed behind the chimney where the smith's mate stood to pump it. On the opposite side to the bellows, at the front of the hearth, stood the anvil, set on a large block of elm wood. The anvil was so positioned that when the blacksmith pulled his hot iron from the fire and turned to the right, he could lay the hot iron straight on the anvil. Swiftness was essential when 'shutting' iron by firing — which is joining two pieces together by melting them in the fire then quickly placing them together and hammering them into shape. It was a skilled job getting the temperature right; too much heat and the iron would fall to pieces, not enough and the join would fail. Both pieces had to be the same heat when joining and the smith would continually pull first one piece and then the other out of the fire until he had them both in the same molten state. Large pieces would need the help of the mate who would go round the front of the troughs and handle one piece onto the anvil, the blacksmith bringing his

The blacksmith's forge.

piece out and laying it on top, then hammering it together till the 'shut' was complete. On the wall nearest the anvil was a shelf which contained a collection of bottom sets which had a square shank which fitted into the anvil. Hanging on the wall were the top sets which matched the bottom sets. These had a handle made of ¼ inch round iron. The bottom set would be put in the anvil then the hot piece of iron would be laid upon it, the top set would be placed on the hot iron and then the mate would strike the lot with a sledge hammer until it satisfied the smith.

Standing in front of the hearth was a swage block about 20 inches square and 6 inches thick. Around the four sides of this were cut shapes of all sorts and sizes and various holes were punched through it to take standard size flat and round iron bar. The bar was first made hot then inserted into the hole that fitted it, then bent; this ensured a fairly accurate bend. The shapes

45

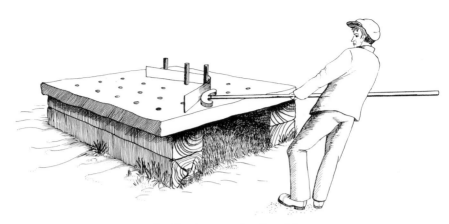

Bending iron on a bending slab.

around the edges of the swage block were to lay the iron on, then hammered into to get the required shape.

In front of the window was a wooden bench about 20 inches wide and 3 inches thick. Attached to the bench at the left end was a large leg vice used by the smiths for various jobs like rasping hot iron threading bolts, sawing and filing. The bench would be covered with a small tool and bits and pieces of work unfinished and waiting for time. The smith was a busy man and had to share his time out to the work in hand and the work to be ready the next day, even the next week. Some pieces of work would perhaps take a week to make but had to be ready when wanted so the smith had to think and work ahead besides the day-to-day jobs that needed doing.

Large double doors opened outward at the end opposite the hearth. Just outside of these stood a large circular mandrel about 4 feet 6 inches high, 2 feet across at the bottom and 3 inches at the top. This had two main uses. One was to make sure anything that had been made circular was a true circle; it was made hot, slipped over the top and tapped until it touched everywhere on the mandrel. The second use was to stretch anything that had been made too small, by heating it and driving it over the tapering mandrel until it was large enough.

A little further outside the double doors was a slab. This was a square piece of iron, 5 feet square by 5 inches thick, set up on wooden blocks which had been buried in the ground. The slab was fastened to these with iron dogs, making a very rigid and sound job. The top face of the slab was about 2 feet off the ground and pierced with 1½-inch holes every 8 inches each way, into which steel pins could be inserted. The other piece of equipment with the slab was the bending bar, which had a curved head, the centre of which had a pin to fit in any one of the numerous holes in the slab. It had a handle of steel 8 feet long and 1½ inches thick and weighed almost one hundredweight. The bar to be bent would be set up against pins, the bending bar would then be put in the nearest hole to the bar with the curved end against the bar. Pulling on the handle would force the curved head to bend the bar round the pin and give it the necessary shape. The slab would also be used to flatten crippled iron, the large flat surface being ideal for this purpose. Along the side of the smithy would be the iron rack which would contain iron of all shapes and sizes, usually in about 18 feet lengths. Various sizes of round iron would be needed for bolt making; half rounds for rubbing bands, flats for all manner of jobs; very large rounds for rudder pins between 2 and 3 inches diameter; large flats for stem bands and other work.

Bolt making was a job that was done when there was a spare hour or so; a lot of the lengths were standard so these could always be made and stored. Bolts came under three categories: dumps, countersunk head and round head. Dumps were plain lengths of round iron, one end of which had been made hot about one inch from the end and then dumped up and down on the anvil until the end had swelled out. These bolts were used for blind fastenings and were driven very tight, the dumped head pulling the two pieces of wood together. For countersunk and round head bolts, the iron was dumped up much more, then made white hot and driven through a die, the dumped up head filling the die and taking shape. The round head bolts needed a top die to form the head; this was held by the blacksmith and struck by his mate with a sledge hammer. Iron knees were hard work in a hand forge but I have seen them made. In fact, I have swung a sledge for hours when extra help was needed in the blacksmith's shop. Heavy rectangular bar was made hot half way along the piece which was to be turned into a knee — white hot — then it would be driven at the ends with the sledge hammer until it was too cool to swell out, then back into the fire to be heated again to be hammered and hammered until it had swollen to the thickness needed. Next, it would be made hot away from this thick part and gradually tapered with a flatter held by the blacksmith and struck by the mate. This would go on until the right taper was obtained each side. While it was still hot, the bolt holes would be punched in with a punch on a handle — again, held by the blacksmith and struck by the mate. After all the holes were punched, it would then be shaped by making it white hot and bending it on the slab, the corner being worked up square when still white hot. It was marvellous the way the blacksmith worked white hot iron, moulding it with his heavy hammers, the intense heat bringing out rivulets of sweat from his brow. Occasionally, he had to wipe it away with the back of his hand which still held the heavy hammer.

The larger ironwork like steering gear, anchor, windlass, winches, pumps, Steering Wheel, gears and cogs and stayfall blocks were made or cast in the local foundries like Gardiner's at the East Kent Ironworks, Sittingbourne and Seager's Ironworks at Faversham.

47

S/B *Favorite.* A very old sailing barge still capable of keeping her cargoes dry.

Chapter III:

Barge Builders On The Swale:
The Sittingbourne Area

The Kentish Swale from Queenborough to Whitstable is now one of the quietest stretches of water to be found along the Kent coast. At the turn of the century it had been one of the busiest, mainly due to the fact that its waters were shallow and fed by numerous creeks whose waters were even shallower but ideally suited for sailing barges and swim head barges. Some of these were fitted out for sailing; in fact, most of the early sailing barges were swimheads. Lee and Eastwoods had many of this type sailing into Conyer. This part of Kent, with its favourable geographical position, its rich soil suitable for fruit growing and its abundance of brick earth for the brick fields, with chalk and mud for the manufacture of cement, sent most of its products away by water. Explosives were made and stored in the marshes around Faversham and much of the hay from these marshes was also taken away by sailing barge. All these industries, vast in their hey-day, needed flat-bottomed craft which could sit in the berths to be loaded without fear of canting over when the tide left them. It was therefore the obvious place to build the sailing barges needed to transport, in bulk, the outputs of these industries.

Of all the barge building sites, Milton Creek was by far the largest, well over four hundred spritsail rigged sailing barges being built on the banks and wharves from the early 19th century onwards. Before the 1820s, the barges built in Milton Creek were small sloop-rigged craft with a number of larger cutter-rigged craft. Some of these were later re-rigged as spritsail barges. One, which had been built by John Huggens and also owned by him, was the *Favorite*, built in 1803.

Favorite, which Captain A. Court told me his father took off the ways about 1921 after having been much rebuilt, had five thicknesses of planks outside and her decks were sheathed with tongued and grooved boards athwartships but she still loaded 125 tons of cement and kept it dry. His father stayed in her for about five years. He maintained that the spelling of *Favorite* was not a mistake but was the old way of spelling it in the early 1800s. On his death, his son, who died in 1969, took over. *Favorite* then was sold to George Smeed. Built at Crown Quay, *Favorite* survived for over one

S/B *Georgina* built by Smeed Deans in 1881 and owned by them, alongside their wharf in Milton Creek.

(Hugh Perks collection)

hundred and sixty years. There were, of course, earlier sailing barges than *Favorite* such as *Industrious Ann* of 1799 and a few others whose records remain. There were about eighteen barge builders on Milton Creek who were well known; there may have been others who perhaps only built one barge or so whose names have been forgotten with the passing of time. Stephen Taylor was building barges in 1825 and, almost a century later, his descendants were still building at Adelaide Dock. F. Smith, William Thompson and James Matthews all had barge yards in the 1820s but the better known builders were R.M. Shrubsall, Mantle, Wills & Packham, Masters, White, W.B. Spencelaugh, Eastwood's and George Smeed (later Smeed, Dean, Burley and Eastwood's), most of whom had businesses in the area.

GEORGE SMEED

The earliest traceable barge of George Smeed was the *Three Sisters* of 1845, although it has been said that he had one built in 1840 when he was twenty years old. The *Three Sisters* was named after three of his daughters. In his lifetime, over one hundred craft passed through his hands, many of them built at his private Murston yard; *Georgiana* of 1852, *Lucretia* 1852, *Mary Ann* 1853, *Florence* 1858, *Alma* 1859. The sprittie *George* of 1852 he named after himself, the *Ellen* of the following year and the *Emily* of 1856 were

50

named after two of his daughters and the *Eliza* of 1857 after another of his daughters. The launching of the *Eliza* on 9th June 1857 was a grand occasion. Afterwards, he invited his shipwrights, sawyers and carpenters to Gore Court House; a cricket match was played and a supper provided afterwards.

Although barges later played the major part in George Smeed's organisation, it is probably fair to say that in the 1850s/60s his concern was with the colliers, principally for the gasworks trade.

The later 1850s to '60s saw Smeed enlarging his fleet of barges but there is no evidence either way as to whether he owned or merely chartered his colliers. The trade, however, was sufficient to warrant his owning a steam tug to tow the vessels in and out of the Swale — essential after the building of Kingsferry Bridge in 1861. The tug he acquired was the *Caledonia* whose engineer was a Mr Thomas Crisp. Towing a barge off Harty Ferry, Crisp slipped and fell into the engine and was mashed up by the machinery.

The new gasworks Smeed planned for Sittingbourne required substantially greater imports of coal. It was laid out with a 1,000-ton capacity coal shed. The gasometer was erected by Cutler & Co., in November 1863, and was connected to the town by an 8-inch main. In readiness for the new works, George Smeed proposed a class of collier with the enlarged hull of a Thames barge and the rig of a coasting schooner. Flat bottomed ketch-rigged barges had probably been built on Milton Creek since the late 1840s and schooner-rigged barges at Faversham since 1854; but these barges had only been 120 registered tons and George Smeed was attempting to build one of 174 registered tons. The big Smeed barges were all built by the master shipwright, Mr F. Sollitt, who came from Chatham Dockyard; later he opened a barge yard on his own account at Rochester. The *Seven Sisters* of 1862 was named after Smeed's seven daughters; at the time, it was the largest vessel built on the creek. Rigged as a two-masted schooner, she was capable of loading 350 tons, her measurements being 116 feet x 23 feet 2 inches by 9 feet 1 inch. She traded to the Humber and N.E. ports with coal and, in 1879, was sold to Doughty of Margate and re-rigged as a brigantine. The Smeed-Sollitt partnership laid down a smaller vessel, the 104-ton *Invicta,* the following year. Her dimensions were 82 feet 2 inches by 20 feet 4 inches by 8 feet 4 inches and she passed to Gill of Rochester in 1879 then to Friend of Margate. In contrast, the *Eliza Smeed* of 1865, which took twelve months to build, was originally a three masted schooner, later re-rigged as a three masted barquentine barge of 347 registered tons. She loaded 750 tons on a 140 feet by 27 feet 8 inches by 13 feet 2 inches hull. On the 14th March 1865, she was launched by Eliza and one of the shipwrights got a free drink when the contents of the launching bottle splashed on his face! Afterwards, a dinner was given to seventy workmen.

Edgar J. March described her as the largest barge in Kent although both *George Smeed* and *Esther Smeed* outclassed her in registered tonnage and

Sarah Smeed at Faversham. (J. Hunt)

carrying capacity. She was built for the coal trade to Rochester. He records how, after putting back to Cardiff leaking in the early 1870s, she was sold to America for the West Indies trade, to be lost in a gale in New Jersey around 1876. Eliza Smeed, who launched her, died in 1867, five months after she had launched the *George Smeed*.

The *George Smeed* of 1866 was also a three masted barquentine of no less than 156 feet by 30 feet 5 inches by 15 feet 1 inch at 477 registered tons. She nearly proved too large to be launched. An attempt was made on the 8th November which failed but an exceptionally high tide on the 10th saw her take the water after a ceremony performed by Eliza Smeed. Surprisingly, in view of the launching of the *Eliza Smeed* the previous year, she was described as 'the first of a new description, built under the superintendence of Mr F. Sollitt as a coaster and foreign-going vessel'. Captain King of Rochester was her master and seemed to be a part-owner. Again, Mr Smeed gave a dinner for his shipwrights. Frank Carr records her sale to Norway on 29th December 1879.

At the time the *George Smeed* was building, Mr Smeed suffered a great personal loss in the death of his daughter Esther Whall and so he had laid down a new vessel in 1868, as commemoration. At 494 tons, the barque-rigged barge *Esther Smeed* was the largest vessel built on Milton Creek, the largest ever built and is said to have carried 800 tons. By the late 1870s, she had been doing regular work to Ireland. Like the other big barges, she carried coal and sometimes worked to the Baltic. It was on charter to the Baltic on the 30th September 1878 that she stranded on the north side of Gotska Sandon, a small island between the Gulf of Riga and Stockholm. Her officers were certificated men and at the following enquiry, Captain James Bennett had his Master's 'Ticket' suspended for twelve months but was allowed to retain a First Mate's 'Ticket'. The Mate, William Hambley had his 'Ticket' suspended for six months. By then, she had been rigged-down to a more manageable three masted schooner.

In 1871, George Smeed built a large coasting ketch barge, the *John Ward*, for the Burham Brick, Lime & Cement Company, named after the company's founder. At 123 registered tons, she traded to Ireland and Belgium.

1872 saw the building of two three masted barges, the 272 registered tons *Emily Smeed* and the 134 registered tons *Ellen Smeed*. The former was 133 feet 3 inches by 25 feet 8 inches by 13 feet 3 inches and she was to survive the longest of the Smeed barges, passing to the Bull Fleet at Newhaven. She was still afloat under jury rig at Lowestoft in 1930.

The *Ellen Smeed* was much smaller, being only 107 feet 8 inches by 22 feet 6 inches by 8 feet 8 inches. By 1880, she had been sold away to Rochester and then to Chas. Marshall, a draper of Faversham, in the early 1890s and with whom she was to remain under Captain Eve until her sale to Scotland in 1912. Here she survived until after the Great War.

The *Emily Smeed* was very much a box-sided affair, fully square rigged on the foremast with very bluff bows and a high bulwark rail and long low quarter boards; the mizzen mast was only slightly shorter than the mainmast.

The last of George Smeed's big barges was the schooner rigged three masted *Sara Smeed* of 1874, 241 registered tons and 125 feet 7 inches by 25 feet 7 inches by 14 feet 4 inches. Again built under Sollitt superintendence, the register records she was partly of second-hand materials — not uncommon in those days — and that the following year she was sheathed with yellow metal, copper fastened, re-surveyed and classed A1 in May 1879. She was off the register in 1882.

It has been said that Smeed's big barges were weak but they were big carriers and his barges had a reputation for being looked after and well maintained. In fact, some considered that he thought more of his barges than he did of his employees.

The big Smeed barges ousted the ketches and schooners from most of the East Coast and Kent ports apart from Faversham and Whitstable. On the spritsail barge side, George Smeed had increased his fleet to fifty vessels by

S/B *Ebenezar* of Smeed Dean Fleet.

1869; of the recent ones, *Meteor* 1869, *Surrey* 1868, *Jane Mead, Wasp* and *Joan* 1866 and *Jessie* 1862 had been from his own yard. When John Huggens died in 1869, George Smeed purchased eight of his barges; some of them fairly old — *Favorite* 1803, *Perseverence* 1824, *Defiance, Elizabeth, Susan and May* and *Water Lily* 1839, *Wave* 1844 and *Isabella* 1840.

For a few years, barge building was only occasional with *Frank* 1870 and *Maud* 1875. In 1875, George Smeed took his manager and son-in-law, Mr G.H.Dean, into partnership. Mr Dean was also described in the directories as being a farmer, fruit merchant and hop grower. Possibly, he also managed George Smeed's agricultural land as it was said that his agricultural investments lost him considerable money. The new firm was constituted as a private limited company, Smeed Dean and Co. Ltd, while Mr Andrews, the foreman, was made a shareholder.

The new company seems to have had an influence on the barge building policy. Some of the older craft were sold or re-built and the yard began to concentrate on the building of spritsail barges. In 1877, the *Hambrook, John Bright* and *Gladstone* were laid down, with *Argosy, Cobden, Derby, Lave* and *Plimsoll* in 1878, *Ebenezer, Vincent, George and Harriet* in 1879, *Burton, Livingstone, Winnie* and *Young Jack* in 1880, *Curlew, Fred, Georgiana* and *Whitehall* in 1881, and *George Smeed* and *Gore Court* in 1882. After *Morley* and *Spurgeon* in 1883, barge production at Murston slowed down to one or two a year. The Deans had often had close associations with members of the Smeed family or local associations. *Young Jack* was named after Jack Dean and *Hambrook* after George Hambrook Dean and the *Ebenezer* after Ebenezer Lodge at the Murston R.A.O.B. The *John Bright* was named after the celebrated 19th century reformer.

In 1878 a public subscription was raised to have Mr Smeed's portrait painted to be hung in the town hall at Sittingbourne. Shortly afterwards, he suffered a seizure and from then on suffered poor health, dying on 2nd May 1881. The following year, the *George Smeed* and the *Gore Court* were laid down to commemorate the man who had made Sittingbourne what it was. Over one hundred craft passed through his hands in his lifetime and, at his death, the company owned about sixty-three barges. After his death, Smeed Dean was to continue building barges for another thirty-two years. Prior to 1894-5, the yard foreman was a Mr Oast who built the *Levitt* (named after one of the yard riggers) and *Maria* 1891, *Lizzie* 1892, *Annie* 1892, *East Hall* 1893, *Leslie* 1894 and probably many of the earlier craft too. He was succeeded by a Mr Palmer who built *Sam* and *H.A.C.* ex-*Invicta* in 1895 and *Elsie* and *Mercy* in 1896. He also started *Graham*. In 1896, Mr Denham took over as foreman, finished the *Graham* and then went on to build *Esther* in 1900, the boomie *S.D.* in 1902 and started the *Harold*. The last foreman, Mr Horsford, finished *Harold* in 1905 and then built *Alan Dean* and *Donald* in 1908 and Smeed Dean's last barge, *Young Garth,* named

One of the repair jobs which came to H.J. Farnington. S/B name unknown. It seems as though the barge had been run down. (Mrs Beard)

H.J. Farnington discussing work to be carried out on a barge with the Master. H.J. Farnington extreme left. (Mrs Beard)

Mrs Irene Beard of Littlestone, Kent, contacted me in 1965 to tell me of her father, H.J. Farnington, shipwright, who served his time with Smeed Dean. Mrs Beard loaned me this photo of her father.

after Garth Doubleday. Much of Horsford's work was in doubling, widening and re-building craft, especially after the Great War when a number of craft, such as *George Smeed* and *Persevere* were re-built, rose on or deepening of the hold by raising the sides; others were re-named after being rebuilt, *Donald* was re-named *V.C.,* Colonel Dean having won this decoration during the war. In 1933, Smeed Dean was taken over by the 'Combine' — Associated Portland Cement Manufacturers — taking over some fifty-two of Smeed Dean's craft, the yard still being used for maintaining their steel lighters.

TAYLOR BROTHERS
The Taylor Brothers built at various places along Milton Creek for seventy-five years. The brothers were shipwrights in their own right. They built something like one hundred vessels during this stay, besides which they were blockmakers and mastmakers and also owned a ropewalk in Milton.

In the 1840s, Stephen Taylor started building barges as well and, in the late 1850s, he re-opened a lower yard at Crown Quay. The firm was then called Taylor Brothers with John running the upper yard which was the original yard. As well as being barge builders, they also owned barges, several of which were built for family ownership.

On 28th August 1862 Sibyl Taylor launched the 150-ton *Ocean Queen* for Knight of Otterham and in October of the same year, they launched the *George & Alfred* of 150 tons from the lower yard, a sister ship to *Ocean*

Queen. These were built for Vandervoord's Southend corn trade. They had dimensions of 75 feet by 19 feet by 6 feet 5 inches.

On 21st February 1863, the *Emily* of 90 tons was launched by Mrs Drake for J.D. Drake. Then, on 9th May 1863, the *William & Mary* became the third barge to be launched that year. She was of 140 tons, built for the 'Stackie' trade for William Murrell, the 'Millionaire Dustman' of London's Dockhead, Bermondsey. She was launched from the upper yard.

Again in October 1863, they launched the ketch barge *Adsey* for C. Wood which was 64 registered tons or 150 tons D.W.T. 1864 saw the coaster *Paragon* of 100 tons, built for Chas. Jordan. She was wrecked at Mablethorpe on 14th August 1889 while bound for Grimsby in ballast. She stranded after leaking; Captain Hadlow, his wife, two children and the crew were rescued. George Mantle, shipwright, was sent by rail to see if she could be got off the beach but all attempts failed.

In 1864 the Taylors built the ketch barge *Maria*. She was converted to a 'sprittie' by 1881 and was owned by C. Wood from 1880 to 1900. Then, in 1865, they built the *John and Edward* and the *Edith Wood,* which were launched on 27th November 1865. The *Edith Wood* was launched fully rigged and was of 96 tons or 200 tons deadweight. She was converted to a sprittie about 1892; a good-looking barge with a clipper bow. The Taylors' output was tremendous. For example, on 5th April 1866, they launched the 100-ton *Foxgrove* for Alf Jordan, then on 2nd June 1866 they launched the *Nore* which was christened by Miss Pym for Alf Jordan's brickworks, which gave them time to get her ready for the Barge Match in five weeks' time. Then they had to get *Fanny Rapson* finished for launching by the 25th June but, being insufficient water on that date, she was not launched until the 2nd July. Later that month, the *Ernest William* went down the ways followed by *Frognal* in the following month. The upper yard (opposite Gransden's Wharf) Crown Quay, which was leased from the executors of John Huggens and managed by young John Taylor, caught fire and was burnt out in August 1866. This did not mean the end of the yard as, later the same year, a coaster, the *Maria,* was built for Burley and launched in November 1866. She was of 150 tons and fated to be wrecked on the Goodwin Sands in January of 1878, laden with pitch.

The following summer their output included the *Venus* and the *Annie Lloyd,* which was launched on the 1st July for Edward Lloyd's newspapers, built to carry straw for the making of paper. On 3rd March 1870, she was washed ashore off Leysdown where her sprit and rudder were lost but the crew were saved. The hulk was eventually towed to Crown Quay for repair.

It says much for the quality of Taylor Brothers' workmanship for, less than four months after her stranding, *Annie Lloyd* went out to win the Topsail Class of the Thames Sailing Barge Match.

After the disastrous fire which burnt out the upper yard, Stephen Taylor kept production going in the lower yard, opening a replacement yard at

Murston, probably in agreement with the newly-formed Burham Brick, Lime and Cement Company, for whom he built a number of barges such as *January* 1868, *February* 1869 and *June* 1869, in which year he handed the yard back to the Company so that they could build their own barges. His replacement yard was then moved to Adelaide Dock. This move could well have been into John Masters' barge yard which had opened in 1866. Although Masters had advertised in the local papers, seeking patronage from local ship owners, he was not very successful and only built a few sailing barges at various sites along the creek wall. Most of his work was subcontracting.

Back to 1867 when the Taylors built the *Thomas & Edward* for Charles Burley and launched her on 26th June. Come 1868, the Taylors were still building to capacity; they built the ketch barge *Mayland* which was lost in a collision with a brig off Happisburgh on 7th November 1897.

Another ketch barge, the *Europa,* was launched on 20th May 1871. She was of 96 tons with a capacity of 200 tons deadweight, built for D.A. Robinson of London, with the dimensions of 100 feet by 22 feet by 9 feet. She was launched by Miss Gill and intended for the cement trade.

Stephen Taylor's activities seem to have ceased initially in the late 1870s, for the next craft he built at the yard were a series of schooner rigged colliers. These were laid down by his brother, John. In order, they were: the 117-ton *Speedwell* of 1883 built for J. Smith, the 117-ton *Magnet* of 1884 built for J. Smith of Burham and launched in May of that year by Sibyl, daughter of Alf Taylor. *Magnet* foundered in 1897. The 133-ton *Vanguard* was launched on 2nd April 1885 by Miss Lottie Taylor. Next was the *Thistle* in 1887 followed by *Queen Mab* of 78 tons or 170 tons deadweight. She was built for James Seagrave and was launched by Mabel Smith. They were followed by the 90-ton *Rochester Castle* of 1889 and the 200-ton *Friendship* of 1890. All except the *Queen Mab* were built for J. Smith of Burham, Coal Merchant, to replace his old fleet of schooners.

By comparison with the barges, the *Thistle* was not a beauty. Her hull length was 105 feet by 23 feet 5 inches beam and a depth of 8 feet 9 inches, able to carry 260 tons. The account of her launching gave her as 105 feet with a depth of 10 feet. She went down the ways dressed from stem to stern, being launched by Miss Ethel Taylor and described by the local paper as 'a fine noble vessel for the coal trade'. In fact, she was very ugly looking, having a large squarish transom, high bulwarks capped with short bow boards forward and long quarter boards aft. She was almost too big for a boomie and had a tall mizzen mast on which she may have set a mizzen topsail.

Edgar J. March records that she was once abandoned off the Scottish coast after a collision and her crew were never heard of again. However, she grounded in the Firth of Tay and was eventually repaired and traded till after the Great War. The schooner rigged *Friendship* could load 420 tons and survived until she was sunk in collision with a collier in the Humber in 1911.

John Taylor's ketches and schooners were said to be weak in construction compared with the barges and were reputed to have cost just over £1,000 per hull for the smaller and £1,200 for the larger ones.

One of his later substantial craft was the 126-ton schooner barge *Emily Lloyd* with a length of 95 feet 8 inches by 22 feet 8 inches, built of 'salted' timbers to A1 Lloyd's Classiciation for 13 years, a very high rating. Her owner was Edward Lloyd of Milton. She traded as far as the Mediterranean for esparto grass. Her master was J. Swan. In 1879, J. Spooner took over as master, in which year she suffered considerable damage. She was later sold to John Smith of Burham and was briefly named *William Levitt* before reverting to her original name.

Some of the other barges known to be built by the Taylor Brothers were the 90-ton *Milton* in 1874, built at the lower yard for C. Wood senior, as a brick barge, and launched by Sibyl Taylor.

On 22nd March from the lower yard, came the *Pioneer* for Pretty and Co., of Milton. On the 29th March, the 90-ton *East Kent* for Scott, the Milton brickmaker. Besides these, on the same day, 29th March 1862, no less than four other barges were being built.

Another well-known barge, the *Warden Court* was launched by Lottie Taylor from the upper yard on 6th July 1870. Of 130 tons capacity, she was built as a 'stackie' and built extra strong for beach work. Her owner was R. Payne of Warden Courts, Warden Point, Sheppey.

On 30th May 1871 she was involved in a great fire while lying alongside Baltic Wharf, Lambeth and was destroyed, along with Markham's Maldon-owned *Defence*. The barges were discharging hay stacks at Landfield's hay wharf. Seven barges were in flames, then the fire spread ashore and burnt out a timber yard and mill. *Defence* must have been an exceptionally well built barge as Law Union Insurance paid out £1,000 on her Taylors' offered £100 for the wreck and towed it back to Sittingbourne where Stephen Taylor spent £500 on rebuilding it.

8th March 1870 saw the *Roberta* of 90 tons launched from Taylors' lower yard by Miss Minnie Taylor for W.M. Levett of Brixton, proprietor of Elmley Cement works.

One of the last barges built by the Taylors was the *Cader Idris*, launched in 1884. The second time Taylors' yard burnt down was in 1870 and a newspaper described it thus: 'Taylors' barge building shed, two-storey building of timber 25 feet high by 80 feet by 35 feet built 1866 destroyed by fire 10th September 1870. Fire put under control by Phoenix Fire Engine. Barge under construction saved.'

Probably the first barge built by the brothers, Stephen and John Taylor, was the *Sittingbourne,* launched 9th September 1857 for J.D. Drake of Scott's Brickfields. She was broken up after the Great Gale of 31st

December 1904 when owned by Ryder. She was carried over the quay and sat on a pile.

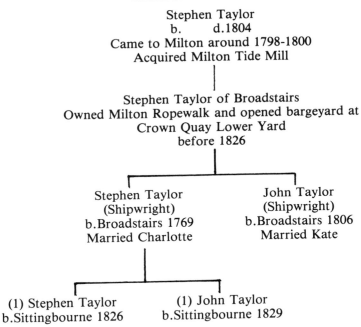

TAYLOR FAMILY TREE

Stephen Taylor
b.   d.1804
Came to Milton around 1798-1800
Acquired Milton Tide Mill

Stephen Taylor of Broadstairs
Owned Milton Ropewalk and opened bargeyard at
Crown Quay Lower Yard
before 1826

Stephen Taylor
(Shipwright)
b.Broadstairs 1769
Married Charlotte

John Taylor
(Shipwright)
b.Broadstairs 1806
Married Kate

(1) Stephen Taylor
b.Sittingbourne 1826

(1) John Taylor
b.Sittingbourne 1829

Note: Brothers Stephen and John took over building from the elder Stephen and John at Upper and Lower Yards in 1856/7. Their first barge is believed to be s/b *Sittingbourne*, 1857.

In 1861, the yard employed 12 men and 7 boys, including:

William Mantle — b.Sittingbourne 1810. Foreman Shipwright
George Mantle — b.Milton 1838. Shipwright
Robert George — b.
Albert Box — b.Milton 1844. Shipwright
James Williams — b.   1843. Shipwright
Alf Horsford — b.Milton 1847. Shipwright
William Read — b.1839. Shipwright
James Boulden — b.Faversham 1823. Sailmaker

ROBERT MARK SHRUBSALL

Robert Mark Shrubsall was born at Milton in 1834, son of Robert Shrubsall, Mariner.

Between 1860-1861 he took over the Milton Wharf Bargeyard which had probably been the site of J. Webster, later Swan and Webster, who operated there 1830-1850.

The first barge he built was the stumpy rigged *Charles* for Charles Wood senior in 1861. In 1862 Shrubsall was busy turning out spritsail barges; on 9th October he launched the *George and Ann* of 100 tons for George Travell of Bobbing, followed two days later by *James*, 120 tons, for W. Barnard of London. Barnard had already had one barge launched on 16th January, the *William and Richard* of 120 tons.

The following year, he launched the *Richard* on the 15th April for C. Wood, launched by Miss Emma Wood. The previous day, Shrubsall had launched the *Quickstep* from his Otterham yard then brought her to Milton to be rigged out. These were followed on 9th May by *Henry* of 100 tons.

In 1864 came the *Maria, Minnie, Robert Stone* and *William Stone*. On 27th April 1865 he launched the *Alpha*, a three masted schooner of 137 tons; it could load 280 tons of cargo and was built for Mr S. Court of Milton, later to pass into the hands of E. Goldfinch of Whitstable. She was later wrecked when under the command of a Captain Sandy. Also in the same year he built a spritsail barge named the *Robert*. In 1866 the *Osprey* and *Lady Flora* of 90 tons for Hodges of Sheerness were followed by the *Bessie Hart* and the *Butcher* for Butcher Gillman & Co. 1967 saw the building of *Alberta* and the *Alexandra*, both for S. Court of Oare, also the *Severn* and the *Roache*. In 1868, the *Rettendon* and the *Clyde*; in 1869, the *Mersey* and the *Richard* and in 1870, the *Tweed* and the *Cryalls*. The *Cryalls* was of 90 tons, built for John Seager of Borden, launched by Miss Seager for Cremer & Seager, brickmakers of Sittingbourne. She capsized and sank at Christmas 1870 off Sheerness, her captain being George Wilson. The barge was raised in 1871. Shrubsall's craft were long and shallow with long runs both fore and aft with very little sheer. *Good Templar* of 1877 had a length of 72 feet with a beam of 17 feet, giving her a very flat look. At one time there was a model of the *Early Bird* of 1879 at the 'Prospect of Whitby' public house in Wapping. His barges were known for their speed and some of the winners of the Thames Matches were *Laura* 1874, *Early Bird* 1879, *Formosa* 1880, *Whimbrel* 1882, *Godwit* 1882, *Gazelle* 1886 and *Pastime* 1890. By 1899 Shrubsall had built about 100 craft, including fishing vessels. Three more of his winning barges were the *Charles* 1861, *Maria* 1864 and *Bessie Hart* which was launched on 31st May 1866 by Miss Wood. The *Bessie Hart* was of 100 tons on a measurement of 75 feet by 16 feet by 15 feet 3 inches; all three of these winners were built for Wood's.

Besides the spritsail rigged barges, Shrubsall built a number of larger craft such as the ketch rigged barges *Mystery* 1875, *Princess* 1871 and *Lord Beaconsfield* 1878. *S.J.B.*. 1888 was of 46 tons ketch rigged and built for

S.J. Brice of Rainham in Kent, who had her in trade for around 50 years. Others included *Genesta* 1887, the schooner rigged barge *Meteor*, rebuilt and lengthened from the *Eclipse* 1863, the *Alpha* of 280 tons, launched on 27th April 1865 and the *Agnes* 1874 of 109 registered tons.

Lord Beaconsfield was originally built as a sprittie. She was 84 feet by 18 feet by 6 feet and was later re-built as a ketch of 58 tons about 1885. She had several owners. In 1881 she was owned by W. Randall of Faversham and later, in 1890, by T. Bassett of Sittingbourne. Her next owner was the well known Osborn Dan of Faversham. In 1907 she was converted back to a sprittie and was owned by R & W Paul of Ipswich. Later still she was sold to Grimsby then, in 1918, she was acquired by Aldous of Arlesford, Essex. *Genesta* was built for T. Bassett of Milton and was of 69 tons. Later, in 1893, she was owned by E. Trussell of Burham. *Agnes* was a schooner rigged barge of 109 tons, loading 200 tons of cargo. She was run down and sunk in 1878.

Meteor was rebuilt from the sprittie *Eclipse* and rigged as a schooner in 1863. She was owned by G. Adams who put her into the coasting trade.

Mystery was built as a sprittie of 61 tons for R. Dobbs of Faversham. She was later converted to a ketch and traded to the Rhine for Apollinaris Water and was later owned by F. Webb of Ipswich. She was converted back to a sprittie and changed hands at Ipswich being bought by a Mr Last. She traded until 1939 and was later used as a housebarge on the Deben.

Robert Mark Shrubsall's other barges (perhaps not all of them) were: *Florence* 1869, *James Bills* 1872, *Anglo-Norman*, *Rachel & Julia* and *Marie Stewart* 1873, *Anglo-Saxon*, *Gertrude*, *Susie* and *Borstal* 1874, *Swiftsure*, *Maud*, *Pall Mall*, *Alice* and *Aldershot* 1875, *Blossom*, *Guy Fawkes*, *Harriet Howard*, *Mistletoe*, *Reliance* and *Sunshine* 1876, *Mary Jane*, *New Ada* and *New World* 1877, *Tees* and *Agreement* 1878, *Constance*, *Fanny* and *Hearts of Oak* 1879, *Red Lancer* and *Myrtle* 1880, *Curlew* and *United* 1881, *Mayflower* 1882, *Britannia*, *Emily* and *B & S* 1883, *Charles & Isabella*, *Heron* and *Charles & Esther* 1884, *Bride* and *Hope* 1885, *Friar Bacon* 1887 *Bluebell* and *R.G.H.* 1891, *Edith & Hilda* 1892, *Chronicle* 1894, *Arthur* and *Charlotte Austin* 1895, *Honduras* 1896, *Company* and *Rathmona* 1897, *Bexhill* and *Tay* 1898, *Magnet* and *Shamrock* 1899, *Bankside* and *Premier* 1900 and *Terror* 1901.

A few of Shrubsall's shipwrights in the early years were: James Pheberg born 1847, George Bonney born 1846, George Davis born 1823 and his two sons, Edward Davis born 1847 and Thomas Davis born 1852.

WILLS & PACKHAM

Wills & Packham took over Taylors' yard in 1889. Here they built and repaired sailing barges until the 1930s. Probably the first barge they built was the *H.T. Wills*, followed by the *W.P.*, also during their first year in the yard. The year 1890 saw the building of *M.M. Packham* and the *Henry & Jabez* who finished her time converted to a houseboat at Conyer, the home

The launch of *Raybel*.

Raybel just after launching.   (A. Cordell)

S/B *Scotsman* at Oare Creek circa 1956.   (Author)

of John and Paddy Nesham and family. She changed hands several times and is now a hulk, still at Conyer. Wills & Packham had large areas of brickfields in the Sittingbourne area so they needed a fleet of sailing barges to transport bricks to London and elsewhere. In 1891 they built three more sailing barges for their fleet. They were the *Ebenezer, Edinburgh* and *Five Sisters. Five Sisters* was also converted to a yacht barge in later life; the owner's wife, Peggy Larken, wrote a book about her. The *Ebenezer* was named after The Ebenezer Lodge of the Good Templars, to which many of the local barge crews belonged. The *Ebenezer* was of 46 tons and the master, when new, was Captain Hobbs whose son, Lawrence, had recently been drowned out of the sailing barge *Security* off the Nore. In 1892 they launched the *Ivy* on 8th May. She was named after Miss Ivy Gull and up to that time was probably one of the best vessels built by them. She was of 90 tons, built for the brick trade and taken when new by Captain Westcott. At the launching her hull was decorated with ivy.

Sailing barge building then seems to have taken a lull. Perhaps the yard had a large repair programme as the next new barge to be built was the *Glasgow* of 35 tons in 1896. She was built as a 'cut' barge or, to most of us, a canal-sized barge, used for taking loads up the canals and able to fit in the locks. She was small but a handy barge to sail. I sailed in her once, many years ago. Her master when new was Captain George Ost who committed suicide aboard her at Gabriel's Wharf, Lambeth in March 1900. I did much work on her around the end of 1938 to 1939 when she came to Conyer to be converted to a yacht barge for 'Bunny' Thorpe.

65

S/B *Raybel* loading at Great Yarmouth. She looks fairly new but it is difficult to date this picture.

(Books Afloat)

S/B *Phoenician* at Great Yarmouth, date unknown.

(Books Afloat)

Once again, another lull in building as the next one to be built was the *Rand* in 1898 followed the next year by *Scotsman*. *Scotsman* was re-rigged a few years ago by the late Wally Buchanan of whose death I have just been informed. Wally was a master rigger; one of the best in the trade. Wally and I worked together once or twice at Liverpool, his home town. From where we were working, we could look across the Mersey and see Cammell Laird's, the yard where he had served his time.

Two sailing barges were launched in 1901, the *C.I.V.*, named after a London regiment, the City Imperial Volunteers and raised for service in the South African War, and the *McKinley*. 1903 saw the launching of *Unique*, which may have been the first of Wills & Packham's composite construction, having metal frames and a wooden skin (outside planking). The later sailing barges built by Wills & Packham were of the coasting type, such as the *Olive May* and *Raybel* in 1920. *Olive Mary* in 1921, later to be renamed *Arcades* and *Phoenician* in 1922. Most of the later barges were fitted with engines and *Olive May* was actually built with an engine. In 1947, *Arcades* was destroyed by fire. I have sailed in *Phoenician* many times in the late 1960s and '70s and found her to be in fairly good condition for her age. She seemed to be permanently moored at Ipswich in those days.

THE OLIVE MAY

Olive May was launched on Saturday, 3rd July 1920. She was a remarkable vessel — and untypical in many ways. For instance, she was designed by Mr H.W. Harvey, a naval architect who supervised her construction. Although a wooden barge with an outer skin of oak and an inner skin of English larch and a deck of Oregon pine she also had a number of features of steel which in the average barge would have been made of wood. Deck carlings, beams under mast deck and her keelson were of steel. The I-shaped girder forming the keelson was packed out with wood. She was given watertight bulkheads.

Unlike most barges, *Olive May* was built with an engine, centrally situated instead of to one side or another of the stern-post. The engine was a 76 h.p. Vickers-Petter, with direct-drive and compressed air for starting (with direct-drive the engine must be stopped and restarted whenever it is necessary to go astern). The bilge pump had two suctions and two deliveries for bilge pumping and washing down her decks respectively.

Her windlass, too, was new. It was called the Harban Patent Windlass, being designed by Mr Harvey in conjunction with Captain Wenban and H. Green, a local engineer. It was a big casting with no bittheads and with two independent warping drums. There was also a dolly-winch incorporated. There were two gears, high and low, for heaving up and the windlass could be taken out of gear when it was necessary to use the two warping drums. The chain came up from the chain-locker below via two big chain pipes, only one of which was normally in use. The weight of the

Olive May prior to launching.

S/B *Olive May* at her launching.

(Alan Cordell)

anchor was held on a band brake, which was released when the anchor was used. The builders, Wills & Packham intended to fit this type of windlass, which could also be adapted for use by motor power, to future craft.

Her 24 feet by 12 feet deckhouse was partly sunk into the deck. The wheelhouse was right aft, with companionways giving access to cabin and engineroom, and had to be kept low so as to clear the boom of her mulie mizzen. This meant that the helmsman had a poor view ahead when the barge was empty, so that when the mizzen was removed in the late 1930s the wheelhouse was raised. It was originally planned to have electric lighting in the engineroom. Initially she had a crew of five. There was also a foc'sle.

Olive May took six months to build, and it was intended that a sister-ship would be laid down directly she was launched. But this did not happen as her cost exceeded the original estimate and Captain Wenban had to sell his ketch barge *Ethel Edith* and the *Beatrice Maud* in order to pay for *Olive May*. Captain Wenban was Managing Director of Kent Coasters Ltd, a consortium of local businessmen. The barge came too late on the scene. She was ordered on a rising market, when good freights were plentiful. By the time she was ready for sea the post-war shipping slump had started, and she never made the large sums predicted. She was still working until the late 1960s.

(This information comes from newspapers and from information given to Pat O'Driscoll, then mate of the barge, by Captain Wenban's daughters in 1965.)

EASTWOOD'S

Eastwood's took over Shrubsalls' yard in 1899 where they built sailing barges for their own use. They moved all their equipment, tools, barge gear and anything else that was wanted in a barge yard, to Milton in one of their sailing barges. Alec Styles served in apprenticeship with Eastwood's at Lower Halstow in 1892. He served under Ambrose Letley. Styles learnt well and turned out to be a very skilled tradesman. He now had the job of running the Sittingbourne yard. His first barge was the *Suffolk* in 1902, followed by *Cheshire* and *Surrey* 1903, *Northampton* 1904, *Bedford* 1905, *Berwick* 1906, *Hereford* 1907 with *Wiltshire* 1908; all of these were for Eastwood's own use. Alec Styles also built the *Edwin* 1903 and *Redshank* also in 1903, both for other owners. After 1908, there were no more barges built although they carried out repairs until 1912 when the yard was taken over by Lloyds, later to become Bowaters, for the repairs to their lighters.

WHITE

White's barge building yard, where some fast sailing barges were built, was situated at the Station Brickworks Dock, which had previously been the yard of Mantle. White had no business interests in the area but was purely a barge builder.

Cremer's *John & Mary* on the wharf at the deep water dock, Oare Creek, after extra high tide and gale force winds. (Eddie Fisher)

He took over in 1890, building both sailing barges and lighters. White's first sailing barge was the *Four Sisters* of 1891. In 1892 White built the *Edith & Hilda*, in 1893 the *Gertrude May* and in 1894 the *Mite* was launched. 1895 saw two more barges launched, the *Vectis* and the *G.W.*, which were followed in 1896 by *Invicta, Clara, Juliet* and *Romeo*. The next year saw even more sailing barges built as, in 1897, he launched the *Windward, Victoria, Vera, T.T.H., John & Mary, Her Majesty* and *Thetis*. *Victoria* was involved in a tragic accident in 1897 whilst racing against *Satanita*, which had been built by White's son who had the Conyer barge yard. *Victoria* was hit by a squall and capsized, drowning the owner, a Mr Austin, and the Captain, Mr Webb.

The *John & Mary* came to Conyer after the Second World War and was converted to a yacht barge for Squadron Leader D.H. Clarke. The barge was in very good condition as we found out after we had winched her up into our shed. She had a double skin of 1½ inch pitch pine which still had that lovely smell after all those years. Nobby (D.H. Clarke) wrote a book about a passage in her; the book was called 'East Coast Passage'.

In 1898 White's yard was again very busy as this year they turned out the *Viper, Vampire, Alarm, Dee, Harry, Maria* and the *Shannon*. *Shannon* came to the Conyer yard to have her bottom doubled in 1937. The crew abandoned her as she came alongside the lower wharf without even bothering to moor her, their kitbags were already packed, their parting words were, 'we've pumped the old cow all the way from Sarthend, she nearly sunk on us twice. Look at these bleeding blisters'. We put her straight on the blocks and when the tide left her, the water ran out of her seams like sheets of glass. She had been in the ballast trade for a long time and her bottom had worn at least to half the original thickness. She belonged to a Mr Peters of Southend at the time.

Only one sailing barge was launched in 1899, the *Silica*. The following year was better as, in 1900, they launched the *Monarch, Mary Ann, Edwin* and *Harold*. *Harold* was named after White's son who had been killed at the battle of Spion Kop in the South African War. At the time it was the largest vessel built by White's. Captain W. Wickens was appointed Master.

1901 saw only one sailing barge launched, the *Edward VII*. None was launched in 1902, but in 1903 they launched *Cecilia, Philippa, Pickwick* and *Sam Weller*. They managed another four in 1904; *Edith, Cutty Sark, Solent* and *Tam O'Shanter*. In 1905, they launched the second *Monarch* and the *Nelson*. In 1906, there was only one launching, the *Queen* and only one in 1907, the *Dreadnought*. In 1908 the *H.M.W.* and in 1910 the *Beatrice Maud*. One other sailing barge built by White was the *Vulture*, but I am not quite sure when she was built. After 1911 the yard was taken over by Mr Harvey.

BURLEYS

The firm of Burleys was founded by Thomas Burley who was born in 1779. His father was a contracting tailor providing uniforms for regiments on contract. He was also a general factor and farmer.

Thomas and his wife, Frances, were blessed with a son, Charles, in 1834. Charles served his time as an apprentice shipwright and was employed by the well-known Taylor brothers. Later, Charles Burley succeeded George Mantle in renting the Station Brickworks Dock barge yard around 1875. He then leased the Dolphin Yard from Smeed Dean in the 1880s.

The Dolphin Yard was used mainly for repairing the firm's barges, a lot of which had been built by Taylor. The Burleys had an interest in bricks, cement and farming, all of which were served by their fleet of sailing barges. In 1866 Taylors had built the *C & B* and the *Fanny Rapson* for Burleys. Mrs Wright, a granddaughter of Charles Burley, told me that Fanny Rapson was a relative of the Burleys. In fact, Mrs Wright showed me the family Bible which had Fanny Rapson's name in it. The *C & B* was built by Taylors for Courtney & Burley, cement manufacturers of Sittingbourne. These two barges were used a lot in the cement trade and about that time Burleys were advertising their cement. The master of the *C & B* in 1883 was Captain Charles Akhurst, his mate was Richard Mills.

F.J. Masters.   (Dolphin Museum)

John Masters.   (Dolphin Museum)

C.T. Masters.   (Dolphin Museum)

Some of the barges reputed to have been built by Burley were *F.B.* and *W.B.* in 1887, *Sydney* 1889, *Stanley* 1890, *May* 1893, *Lawrence* 1896, *Dorothy* 1898 and *Charles Burley* 1902. Other barges owned by the Burleys were *Annie Bryan* 1876, *Cecilia* 1876, *Clara* 1873, *Edith* 1882, *Fannie Maria* 1864, *Foxgrove* 1866, *Spring* 1860 and *Vectis* 1895. Some of these could have been built by Burley, the *Vectis* was, of course, built by White of Sittingbourne. Like all barge owners, Burleys had their losses. *F.B.* was run down by the steam yacht *Albion* off Gravesend in March 1878. *Maria*, built by Taylors for Burleys, was of 150 tons capacity and was wrecked on the Goodwin Sands on 29th January 1878, loaded with 137 tons of pitch from Milton to Dunkirk. She was under the command of Captain Gray. All the crew were saved by the lugger, *Champion*.

Charles Burley and his wife, Frances, were blessed with a son, also named Charles. This son married the daughter of Captain H.W. Shore, master of the Sheerness hoy barge, *Factor*. Charles Burley senior died at the Bull Hotel, Sittingbourne in July 1891.

OTHER BARGE BUILDERS
William and George Mantle operated a barge yard from the 1830s to 1875. William Mantle was born at Sittingbourne in 1810 and was a shipwright for Taylors and later became foreman shipwright at Taylors in the 1850s. He left Taylors in 1866 to lease John Huggens' former Station Brickworks Dock barge yard on Huggens' death. William was later succeeded by his son, George, born at Milton in 1838, who had previously been employed as a shipwright with Taylors. George was declared bankrupt in 1884 — not an unusual thing in those days. His barges were put up for sale by Jackson & Sons (Auctioneers) in January 1885. The *Roberta* fetched £245, *Revetta* was sold to George Hodgekins for £300, the *Frank* £505, *Ursula* was bought by Mr Butler for £300 and the *Alfreda* was unsold.

Some barges built by Mantle were the *Conyer* 18.4.66 and the *Murton* 1866, both for H. Chambers. On 20th February 1875 he launched the *Maud* of 95 tons capacity, built for H. Lavers and launched by Claud Mantle. In January 1884 he launched the *Preston* which loaded 120 tons, built for Prior, Brain and Perry of Faversham Brickworks. The *Gypsy* and *Providence* were both launched in 1877 and *William & Eleanor* in 1873. It was also thought that he built a barge called *Rochester* of 34 tons.

John Masters was born in 1820. He had two sons, Charles born in 1846 and John born in 1851. He advertised as 'Shipwright, Barge and Boat Builder, Shipsmith, Mast, Spar, Oar and Block Maker at Adelaide Dock'. His barges included the *Charley*, built in 1870 and launched from Adelaide Dock. She was built for J.D. Drake and was launched by William Drake. Masters also built at Crown Quay at Filmers Dock and various places along the creekside, even a seawall.

A seawall built barge. (Dolphin Museum)

All that remains of *Band of Hope* pulled out of the mud at Butterfly Wharf, Conyer, when the seawalls were strengthened. (Author 1965)

Young John Masters carried on the trade as a block maker but his brother, Charles, served his time as a shipwright. In 1884, they built another barge for J.D. Drake which took him and his apprentice four years to build. The *Helvellyn* of 125 ton capacity. The *Sidwell* was built in 1877, *J.D. Drake* in 1898 and the *Sara & Eliza* in 1880. The 1871 Census shows that John Masters, aged 51, was a shipwright; Charles, 25 years old, was also a shipwright and John Masters was a blockmaker, aged 20 years.

Spencelaugh built at Crown Quay lower yard in the 1870s to 80s. Their barges included the *Thomas and Frances* 1878 and the small *Band of Hope* 1878 which finished her days at Conyer, belonging to Eastwood's as a mud barge. Her remains laid on the Butterfly Wharf for years. Loaded with coal, she capsized off Eastchurch in the Swale, after her leeboard touched when coming about. The crew were rescued by the Eastchurch rescue boat which was always in the area in case some of the airplanes had to 'ditch' into the sea. She was salvaged and Eastwood's then used her for a mud barge. I went on board her in the early 1930s. She had been laid up, as Eastwood's were then using a larger barge for their mud work.

Milton Creek Barge Builders
1820-30	William Thompson built dumb lighter
1820-30	F. Smith then Charles Smith
1827	James Matthews
1820-4	George Peak

In 1847, W. Thompson had changed to sailmaking. His son, William, born in 1828, was also a sailmaker at Quay Lane, Milton.

Milton Wharf Barge Yard
1830s	J. Webster
1840-50	Swan & Webster
1861-99	Robert Mark Shrubsall
1899-1920	Eastwood's Brickmakers Ltd
1912-37	Lloyd's as a repair yard then . . .

Station Brickworks Docks
1790-1865	John Huggens
1866-75	George Mantle then William Mantle
1875-90	C. Burley
1890-1920	Whites
1920-38	Wills & Packham
1938-53	Sittingbourne Shipbuilding Company

Filmers Dock
1866-69	John Masters

Sailing barge *Oak* being repaired at the Dolphin Barge Museum, Sittingbourne.

(Hugh Perks Collection)

Dolphin Yard

1890-1965	Burley
1970-77	Working Museum, then re-opened

Adelaide Dock

1845-77	George Smeed
1860-69	Burham Brick, Lime & Cement Company
1869-80	John Taylor
1880-1915	Alf Taylor
1877-1932	Smeed Dean
1932-65	A.P.C.M.
1937-47	Alfred Wood

S. Dane was also operating in the Milton area.

Chapter IV:
Barge Builders On The Swale:
Other Areas

CONYER

Tucked away at the head of a small creek on the North Kent marshes, between the towns of Sittingbourne and Faversham, lies the small hamlet of Conyer in Teynham. Its origin is lost in antiquity but it was certainly habitated by the Romans who were probably the first people to be aware of its usefulness as a port. It has been much altered since the Roman times by the enwalling of the surrounding marshes, which created a narrow waterway whose channel is kept clear of silt by two streams which enter the head of the creek at opposite sides through self-closing sluice gates.

It was to this busy little backwater that, in the early 1860s, came one John Bird to carry out his trade as a shipwright. John Bird, one of four sons, was born on 10th April 1832. His elder brother, James, was born on 27th May 1829. The other brothers were William, born 12th May 1834 and Frank, born 22nd November 1836. It was thought that, at one time, the family lived in Conyer Farmhouse, as an entry in the family Bible states that John was kicked by a horse and received a broken jaw, had three teeth knocked out and a two-inch cut in his chin. The entry was dated 2nd December 1844 and his age given as twelve and a half. All of this information came to me through a relative of John Bird, the late Mr Goddard, who had contacted me after reading my book, 'Just Off The Swale', to tell me that I had mis-named his great grandfather as Josiah Bird instead of John Bird. In fact, for many years, I had believed that it was Josiah and the directories gave it so, but directory entries are often copied year after year and any mistakes therefore perpetuated. Thanks to Mr Goddard, the record is now corrected.

Mr Goddard presented me with indisputable evidence that it was in fact John and not Josiah. In his possession he has numerous papers and indentures of John Bird. What John Bird did for a living after leaving school is not clear but it is known that, at one time, he was in the Police Force and it was not until he was twenty-five years old that he decided to become a shipwright, serving his time with Smeed, but with a difference as his indentures were only for five years instead of the usual seven. Perhaps his age at starting had something to do with this.

It is difficult to decide how long after his time finished with Smeed that he started on his own as a master shipwright. One of the possessions in Mr Goddard's collection is a penny notebook in which John Bird had made numerous entries, the earliest being 1861 when he would still have been serving his time at Smeed's yard. The first entry is as follows, spelling and capitals as written in John Bird's own handwriting, which at times needs a lot of patience to interpret:

May 27 1861
Commenced layin Down a large Schooner
Putickulers of Demontions Length on the Keel 105 feet 8 inch
Length over all 113 feet ½
Breath of beam first square flower from forward 23 feet on the bottom 21 feet after square *flower* back 22 feet 10 inches Bottom 20 feet.
Size of Ih 11 by 7½ size Sm 11 by 13 size Sh 14 by 10
Lent of stem 13 feet Rake 6 in in 12 feet
Lent of stern post 13 feet Rake 6 in in 12 feet
Hiegh of Transom from bottom of Keel 17 feet 6 inches size 8 in by 12 in
Size of flower Timbers 7½ by 10 size of upright 8 by 7½ and 7½ by 6½
Bottom plank 4 in Thick in the flat Length of flat ?
Breadth of Beam Midship 23 feet Reg Tons 224 length of ???? over 7 feet ½
Counter timbers Sided 7 by 8 in Moulded 34 flower timber on flat 14 in by 12 in the clear 9½ in sided fore and aft flat plank 4 in thick on bends 3 in end work Make Able Timbers between ever other timber framing nearly all done by August 7 on the keelson in witch is 12 by 16 in Hoging piece on top 10 in Deep Making in all 26 in by 12
S by September 24 the Bends were all worked in strakes of 4 in plank
Chime work is the same as small barge and the first seam rabbet, tar and hair.
In Depth of Side over all 10 feet 2 inches Breath of beam over all 24 feet
Decks on Nov 2nd 3 in by 7 in
Decks all in and caulked by Nov 9th 3 day work for 11 men
Hatch Ways Fore 4 feet square Mane 12 by 8 feet After 11½ by 7½ feet
Mast fore 52 feet 6 in Main 54 feet 6 in Misin 49 feet
Measurement tonnage 173 Tons Seven Sixtens Milton Port of Faversham
gangways The between hatchways 8 in by 4 in
Cabin Companion
Cabin ??? length
forecastle Hatchway
Waterway 3½ in thick Covering board in tow peices 3 in by 8 each
Spargin peices forward 8 in deep aft 4 inches
two side keelsons 12 by 7 in 3 lenth taper it of each end 3
????? ????? Main Hatch
2At6 by 6 join shape knee between every beam
Rudder 5 feet Long on the ???? sise of post but all joint up by Nov 21st

*flowers means floors

The second account in his notebook concerns the *Garibaldi* of 1862, by which time John Bird would have been out of his time at Smeed's. He must have been responsible for laying down the *Garibaldi* at Murston, as there is no account of timber used; was he by then on his own and sub-contracting for building labour costs only? He appears to have paid his workmen almost daily as though he hired them as and when he needed them. It is generally thought that Sollitt built the *Garibaldi* at Smeed's but here is an ancient document that may change one's thought as it implies that J. Bird was in charge.

'*Name The Garibaldi*
Commenced to build a large barge about 150 tons Burden about the 1st April 1862 length of keel 82 feet Breadth of bottom 17 feet 6 inches on beam 18 feet 8 inches length of fore flat 20 feet length of after flat 21 feet with of stern frames 10 feet lift of stern 9 feet 6 inches size of keel 9½ by 4½ ??? 3 inches chines 4½ thick flower timber 7¼ by Uprights 8½ Bottom 3 inches thick sides 2 inches streak next top 2½ inch top one 3½ thick keelson 12 inch by 11 sided 7 by 8 Double Frame Each End Depth of side overall 7 feet length overall 84 feet in fram about 17th May 1862 Cost of framing Excluding fasting the bottom to gether £27..15..9 To patent Double Action Windlas put in by J Bird 9 day work at 4s and 6d a day £2..0..8d Fisished and Launched October 6th 1862'

Without a doubt, the *Garibaldi* was named after Giuseppe Garibaldi (1807-1882). The son of a poor fisherman, he was born at Nice. When he grew up, he became a sailor and it was not until 1834 that he showed signs of being a rebel by joining the 'Young Italy' movement, then spent the rest of his life working for the unification of Italy; at the time, Italy was a number of small states and kingdoms, each with its own ruler.

Garibaldi raised an army and led it to victory and eventually, Italy was united, the King of Sardinia, Victor Emmanuel, being crowned King of Italy in February 1861. One can read the fascinating life of Garibaldi in G.M. Trevelyan's trilogy: 'Garibaldi's Defence of the Roman Republic', 'Garibaldi & the Thousand', 'Garibaldi and the Making of Italy'.

Garibaldi came to England on a visit in 1864 and was seen as the symbol of freedom and democracy. A remarkable military leader, he was well received by the British and this probably accounts for why there were two or three barges named Garibaldi built around this time.

Estimate for the *Garibaldi*
(Spelling and final addition still as J. Bird wrote it)

Istemate for a Barge 82ft Long 18ft Beam 5 feet 6 Side	
Laying Blocks Stem Sternpost Keel Dead wood. 12 days.	3.. 0.. 0
Laying bottom 20 day puting the sternframe	
Niblings Harpins	8.. 0.. 0

Framing the bow ends 36 day Amidships 24 Days	15.. 0.. 0
Making able Timbers 12 fastenin 4 Days	
Treenailing Bottom 4 Days	5.. 0.. 0
Trimming Down getting Rabbet out 14 Days	
working out flats 48 Days	15.. 0.. 0
Scining up the sides III Dressing Down Treenails 5 days	29.. 0.. 0
Triming out inside 4 Days Shelf Brest	
Hook quarter knees 16 Days	5.. 0.. 0
Framing Top 24 Days plank ?? filling in 14 Days Deck 16 Days	13..10.. 0
Caulking 20 Days Windlass 5 Days Bits ??	
Knee 5 Days Bowsprit Bit ?? 2 Days	8.. 0.. 0
Mast Case 4 Days Main and fore Hoss 4 Days	
Scuttle Hatch 1½ Days for Hatch 2 Days	2..17.. 6
Main Hatch 4 Days Making Do 5 Days Buby	
Hatch skylight Scuttle Ha 9 Days	4..10.. 0
Wash Strake 10 Days Cleat Chock 4 Days	
Stem Band Mold Chainplate ?? snatch	5.. 5.. 0
Leaboards 8 Days Rudder Irons Do Posts 10 Days	
Eye Bolts @ Co 6 Days	6.. 0.. 0
Main Kelson 5 Days Chine Do I 0 Days	
Sealin 8 Days Lining 8 Days	7..15.. 0
Cabbin 24 Days Forecastle 6 Days including Bulk Head	7..10.. 0
Launching 8 Days	2.. 0.. 0
Quarter Boards 6 Days	1..10.. 0
	£137..17.. 6

The above are accounts copied from John Bird's day book. John Bird's stay at Conyer covers almost a quarter of a century during which his son, Albert, served his time under his father but being made to serve his full seven years. Sometime after finishing his apprenticeship, the government needed shipwrights to sheath a large warship which needed many hands used to this kind of work. These were recruited from the bargeyards and Albert was among them. Preferring this kind of work to barge building, he never returned to his father's barge yard but joined the staff of Sheerness Dockyard. John Bird's other son, John, also served his time under his father.

During John Bird's stay at Conyer he built over thirty sailing barges and probably some lighters or dumb barges. Repairs and rebuilding went on all the time; probably this is the reason there are gaps at various times when no new sailing barges were built.

As well as being a barge builder, John Bird also owned and worked sailing barges with paid crews. His notebook contains records of freights carried and the barges' names and some of the captains' names but, the most interesting thing is the amount of money each freight earned and the

Form No. 10.

BILL OF SALE.

| Official Number of Ship | 707 | Name of Ship | Collier Quest |

Port Number and Year of Registry: 7852

Port of Registry: *Rochester*   British or Foreign built: *British*

Number of Decks	One
Number of Masts	One
Rigged	Sprit Sail
Stern	Square

Build: *carvel*
Galleries: *none*
Head: *none*
Framework: *wood*

No. of Engines.   Particulars of Engines (if any)

How propelled: *by Sail*   Where built: ...   When built: ...

Length, from forepart of Stem, under the bowsprit, to the aft side of the Head of the Stern-post - - - - 70 ft. 4 tenths
Main-breadth to outside of Plank - - - - 14 ft. 6 tenths
Depth in Hold from Tonnage Deck to Ceiling at Midships - - 4 ft. 3 tenths
Depth in Hold from Upper Deck to Ceiling at Midships in the case of three Decks and upwards
Length of Engine Room, if any

| Diameter of Cylinders | Length of Stroke | No. of Horses' Power combined |

When made.   Name and Address of Makers

Whether British or Foreign made.

GROSS TONNAGE.

| | No. of Tons. |
| Under Tonnage Deck | 31.86 |
| Closed-in Spaces above Tonnage Deck, if any, Space or Spaces between Deck — |
| Poop |
| Forecastle |
| Roundhouse |
Other closed-in Space, if any, as follows — Break	2.8
Gross Tonnage	34.8
Deductions as per Contra	32.94
Registered Tonnage	32.94

DEDUCTIONS ALLOWED.

On account of Space required for Propelling Power
On account of Spaces occupied by Seamen or Apprentices, appropriated to their use, and kept free from Goods and Stores of every kind not being the personal property of the Crew. These Spaces are the following, viz.:

Total Deductions

No. of Tons.

I John Usher of Faversham in the County of Kent *Mariner* ....
in consideration of the Sum of Seventy five pounds .... paid to I *me* by John Bird of Chester Stephens
in the County of Kent Ships Builder ....
the Receipt whereof is hereby acknowledged, transfer Thirty Six 64/64 Shares in the Ship above particularly described, and in her boats, guns, ammunition, small arms, and appurtenances, to the
said John Bird ....

Further I John Usher ...... the said John Usher .... for I *myself and my* heirs covenant with the said
John Bird .... and I *his* .... and I I *have* power to transfer in manner aforesaid the premises herein before expressed to be transferred,
and that the same are free from incumbrances**

In witness whereof I *have* hereunto subscribed *my* name, and affixed *my* seal this sixth day of May .... One thousand eight hundred and Eighty four.

Executed by the above-named John Usher ....
in the presence of J. J. Brindley ....

John Usher ●

No. 40?

FBT 12,560 3-82 (10——) 124

Handwritten note in margin: 1884 May 15th ...

S/B *Colingwood* in the Thames, January 1881. (Pat O'Driscoll collection)

expenses incurred. One of the papers in the John Bird collection is an agreement to buy a half share in the sailing barge *Collingwood* from John Usher of Faversham dated 6th Day of May 1884.

I have taken a few examples of accounts on different barges run by Bird; these barges must have been bought by Bird and repaired at his Conyer Yard then put to work to earn money to establish the Yard to barge building. Probably this is why no barges appear credited to Bird before 1865 as he may have been repairing barges for his own use. Some of the Smeed entrepreneurial spirit must have rubbed off on Bird during his apprenticeship.

A/C To Barge *Tombs* (or *Tomby*)

					Master's expenses on freight
June	4	freight of:	bricks	£5..14.. 0	3.. 0
July	24		bricks	4..12.. 3	4.. 0
			ashes	3..14.. 0	2.. 0
			coals	2..15.. 0	2.. 0

August	7	bricks	3..18.. 4	2.. 0
		ashes	5.. 4.. 0	3.. 0
August	23	sand	4..19.. 9	£1.. 5.. 0

A/C To Barge *Acorn*

July	13	freight of: bricks	£5.. 8.. 3	3.. 0
		to demmurge	10.. 6	
		freight of: manure	7.. 0.. 0	£1.. 5.. 5
		bricks	5.. 2.. 0	3.. 6
		manure	7.. 0.. 0	1.. 5.. 5
August	17	bricks	6.. 3.. 5	7.. 6
		coke	4.. 7.. 5	7.. 6
August	28	bricks	5.. 3.. 5	7.. 6
		manure	7.. 0.. 0	1.. 5.. 5
Sept	5	iron	8.. 0.. 2	1.. 4.. 0

Here, the barge's name cannot be understood owing to the inconsistency of Bird's handwriting:

A/C To Barge *????*

July	9	freight of: manure	£7.. 0.. 0	£1.. 5..10
	16	corn	9.. 0.. 6	1.. 0..11
	24	sand		
		94 yd	6..14.. 0	1.. 9.. 0
		bricks	5..14.. 0	17.. 9
		ashes	4..17.. 6	8.. 0
August	23	bricks	5..19.. 6	1.. 8.. 0
	24	lalic*		
		80 tos	18.. 0.. 0	4.. 9.. 1
		to dummurge	1..11.. 6	

*In Bird's handwriting, this looks like Lalic but could be Salic or any word. It was an expensive cargo, needing extra time to unload and therefore demmurrage had to be paid.

A/C to Barge *Eliza May*

August	8	freight of: bricks	£5.. 8.. 3	19.. 6
		manure	4..15.. 0	5.. 6
August	19	bricks	5.. 4.. 0	5.. 6

This account was separate from the others, being the Conyer Account which seems to imply that Bird was running the Conyer Yard as well as building barges elsewhere.

			£..s..d
June	15	Paid on account Conyer	8.. 2.. 8
		for Nails	1.. 6
		Ben	.. 8
		????	3.. 6
		Labourers	2..18.. 8
		Box*	1.. 0
		Pout	12.. 0
		Carrage	4..11
		Moor	8.. 0.. 0
		Paint brushes	4.. 4
		to labour	3.. 5.. 6
A			
June	24	to Moor	1.. 0.. 0
		Carrage	.. 9
		Taylor rope	8.. 8
		Dick Hans	5.. 0
		???? Elm	2.. 6
		Ben Lane	..11
		Mr Watts	1.. 0.. 0
	30	Labours	3..17.. 0
July	5	Mrs Sharps Bill	1.. 1.. 2
	8	Sawyers	16.. 0
		Han	1.. 0.. 0
		Mrss Ladder Bros	10.. 0.. 0
		Travelling	5.. 0
	9	Rail Carrage	4.. 9
	10	400 Treenails	1.. 2.. 0
	11	Rail Carrage	7.. 6
		Lounce for trip	2.. 6
	13	Sawyers	1..10.. 0
		Han	10.. 0
	18	Fimby Lounce	1.. 0
	20	Sawyers	1.. 0.. 0
		Han	1.. 0.. 0
	24	Lamp Oil	4.. 6
		Traveling	2.. 0
	28	Sawyers	2..12.. 0
	31	Mrss Broad & Lachfors	10.. 1.. 0
B			21..19.. 5
August		to travelling	7.. 0
	3	Fimby Lounce	2.. 2.. 7
		Lounce	1.. 0
		Sawyers	2..16.. 0
		Han	17.. 0

85

	5	Lounce	1.. 6
		Fimby Lounce	1.. 6
		Moor	3.. 6
		to ?????	2.. 6
		Sawyers	2..14.. 0
		Han	1.. 0.. 0
		Lover	17.. 6
		Surtiss	2.. 6
		Ben Fimby Lounce	3.. 4
	17	Sawyers	2..10.. 0
		Han	1.. 0.. 0
		Moor	2.. 0.. 0
		Nails	5.. 6
	20	Ben Fraburn	1.. 4
	22	New Lock	2.. 0
		Boyers	16.. 4
		Lounce	1.. 4
		Moor	5.. 0
	24	Moor	5.. 0.. 0
		Sawyers	2..13.. 1
		Han	1.. 0.. 0
		Moor	1..10.. 0
		Mrss Ladder Bros	10..11.. 4
		Mr Finney	13..16..10
		Mrss Rowns & Co	10.. 1.. 0
	26	Felins	4.. 0
		Pair of Ower (pair of oars)	5.. 0
		???????	1..16.. 2
		Box of bolts	1.. 0
	31	Sawyers	2..14.. 0
		Han	1.. 0.. 0
		Moor	1.. 7.. 0
Sept C	2	Lime	11.. 0
Sept	2	Lounce	1..10
	2	Munfs	2.. 6
	5	Lounce	1.. 8
	5	Lutton	4.. 0
	5	Moor	5.. 0
	5	Parcel Carrage	1.. 3
	5	Sawyers	2.. 0.. 6
	5	Han	1.. 0.. 0
	5	Moor	1.. 0.. 0
	11	Whatt	19.. 0

13	Lounce	2.. 0
13	Boy	1.. 1
13	Moor	7.. 0
15	Sawyers	1.. 4.. 0
15	Han	1.. 0.. 0
15	Lounce	1.. 8
16	Mrss Brown	25.. 0.. 0
16	to Travel	5.. 0
17	Boulden	5.. 0
		34.. 6..11
17	Sawyers	6.. 9
18	Taylor	1.. 1.. 0
18	Boulden	9.. 0
18	Lounce	1..10
21	Sawers	1..14.. 0
21	Han	1.. 0.. 0
21	Moor	1.. 1.. 0
21	Bowes	1..16.. 0
27	Book	5.. 3
27	Beer	.. 6
27	Taylor	14.. 6
		8.. 9..11

JOHN BIRD'S CONYER ACTIVITIES

It is not known if John Bird was the first man to build barges at Conyer, certainly fishing smack and oyster boats must have been built there but they required much less space on which to build. I think we can assume that John Bird was the first man to build any quantity of sailing barges at Conyer.

There was a sailing barge named *Rose* built at Conyer in 1866, the year that Bird started to build at Conyer; I have every good reason to think that he was at Conyer two or three years earlier repairing barges.

The *Rose* of 1866 was built for Osborn Dan, Flint Merchant of Faversham. In 1904 the *Rose* struck a buttress of Waterloo Bridge and sank. Bird next built a small barge of 28 tons, the *Harry*, built in 1868, once again owned at Faversham by Mr Fred Bunting. Also in that year he built the *Walter* of 34 tons for F. Burgess of Camberwell. *John & Eliza* of 38 tons was next in 1869, owned by E. Killick of Northfleet. She was followed by *Equivalent* of 36 tons in 1871, owned by Samson Dan. Her remains lie in the East Swale near Faversham Creek. *Mabel* of 39 tons, launched in 1873, was owned by Rowley Richardson of London, later by Turner of Rochester before the First World War. She was followed by *Jeffie* in 1874, again of 39 tons, owned by W. Richardson of Vauxhall. Captain Fred Harris of Conyer had this barge for some years. Also in 1874 the *Lydia* of 40 tons was launched. Again, she was owned by W. Richardson.

Whites Conyer bargeyard in 1976.   (Author)

Charles Hutson around 1935. One can see that she was worked hard. Was the mate below making tea?   (Alan Cordell)

John Bird's next barge was also for W. Richardson in 1876. She was the *Phoebe* of 39 tons; later sold to Penfold's of Greenwich and still trading in the 1930s. His second barge in that year was the *H.C.* of 45 tons, owned by Covington of Pimlico and named after Henry Covington. In the same year he launched a bigger barge, the *Eustace*, of 76 tons, ketch rigged and owned by Westwood of Millwall.

In 1877 Bird launched the *M.A.C.* of 47 tons, another one for Covington's of Pimlico who obviously did not believe in wasting money on carving names, only initials. Another big barge built that year was the *May-Hawthorn* of 75 tons, owned by Phelande-Garrod of 19 Bussel Street, Ipswich. In later years she was re-named *Mocking Bird*. She was sold to Goldfinch of Whitstable and finally broken up at Denton, Gravesend, in 1950.

In 1878 came *Rosa* of 36 tons, owned by Fred Bunting of 34 Cyprus Road, Faversham. She later passed into the hands of Sheppey Glue Works. In the same year the *Elwin* of 38 tons was launched for Southchurch Brickfields in Essex and later owned by S. Johnson of Brompton Lane, Strood. The final one for that year was the *Ethel* of 45 tons owned by C. Gutteridge and later by Parker of Bradwell, Essex, to carry haystacks from Essex.

Albert and Ellen came in 1879, of 39 tons and owned by A. Anderson of Randell Street, Maidstone. Also in that year, came the *Violet* of 39 tons, built for Covington of Pimlico. In 1880 came *Josephine* of 44 tons, owned by C. Wright of Maidstone. *Amy* followed in the same year, of 39 tons and owned by Goldsmith's of Grays, Essex. The following year came the *Nellie Maud* of 43 tons, built for C. Tolhurst of 17 East Street, Faversham, later to be owned by the Kent Stone Company and to survive into the 1930s. She was followed by the *Edwin and Emily* of 45 tons, owned by S. Killick of Northfleet, later by the Associated Portland Cement Company Limited in the early 1930s. Also in 1881 came the *Lizzie* of 40 tons, owned by Westwood of Millwall and later by Robert Mercer of Rodmersham and even later by Burley. She was burnt at Milton Creek in 1952.

John Bird built four barges in 1882. The first was the *Dan* of 42 tons, owned by Westwood of Millwall, later by H. Cunis of Purfleet. Next came *Sara Louisa* of 43 tons, owned by Mrs Emily Nicholls, 30 Manor Park, Lee, and later by Grundy of Southend. *John & George* followed of 40 tons, owned by Westwood of Millwall, later by G. Wright of 36 Plough Road, Rotherhithe. The last one for that year was the *Guy*, also owned by Westwood of Millwall, later sold to Cunis.

In 1884 came the second barge to be named *Violet*, usually referred to as *Mercer's Violet*. She was 42 tons, owned by Westwood's of London, later sold to Mercer, and she ended her days hulked in Hoo Creek. *Violet* was followed by *Hilda* of 43 tons and then a gap of four years before the next

Frank Hinchly, probably taken about 1888 towards the end of his apprenticeship at Birds yard at Conyer.   (Brian Hinchly)

building. In 1888 came the 45 ton *Isabel*, owned by Westwood of Napier Yard, Poplar and later by A. Rawlinson of East Ham.

The last barge built by Bird was in 1889, the *Charles Hutson* of 56 tons, owned by J. Lee of Strood, later by W. Smith of Framlingham, Suffolk and, later still, by Horlocks of Mistley, Essex. Subsequently she became a houseboat at Pin Mill; she was converted in 1941 and is now derelict on the foreshore in front of the 'Butt & Oyster' public house.

I had given up all hopes of acquiring any more information on John Bird until I received a telephone call from Brian Hinchley of Burwell, Cambridge. He informed me that his grandfather had served his time under John Bird and, as he was on a cycling holiday, could he come to see me? Of course, I was delighted and arranged for him to visit me. Brian had already done the research on his grandpa which saved me a lot of time. His grandpa's name was Frank Burt Hinchley — Burt being his mother's maiden name. He was born 19th November 1868 at 41 Tanner Street, Faversham, the youngest son of five children of Daniel and Harriet Hinchley, Cabinet Makers, Upholsterers and Paper Hangers of 29 West Street, Faversham. By 1888 Frank's family had moved to 29 West Street, having moved from 87 Abbey Street. Frank finished his apprenticeship in 1889, having started it in 1883. He must have been 15 years old when he started, therefore, only serving six years (it was seven when I did mine), even his pay was better all those years ago. His money for the:

first year was   9 shillings a week
second year was 10 shillings a week
third year was 11 shillings a week
fourth year was 12 shillings a week
fifth year was 13 shillings a week
sixth year was 14 shillings a week

This Indenture Witnesseth That

Ann Tunley

Son Francis Tunley Tunley Born in Flixton near to 766

doth put and bind herself Apprentice to John Bird

to learn his Art and with his after the Manner of an Apprentice to serve from the 21st May last after 1838

unto the full End and Term of Six Years from thence next following to be fully complete and ended. During which Term the said Apprentice his said Master faithfully shall serve his secrets keep his lawful commands every where gladly do. He shall do no damage to his said Master nor see to be done of others but to his Powers shall tell or forthwith give warning to his said Master of the same. He shall not waste the goods of his said Master nor lend them unlawfully to any. He shall not contract Matrimony within the said Term nor play at Cards or Dice Tables or any other unlawful Games whereby his said Master may have any loss with his own goods or others during the said Term without License of his said Master. He shall neither buy nor sell. He shall not haunt Taverns or Playhouses nor absent himself from his said Master's service day or night unlawfully. But in all things as a faithful Apprentice he shall behave himself towards his said Master and all his during the said Term.

And the said

his said Apprentice in the Art of Shoemaking

that he on shall teach and instruct or cause to be taught and instructed. Finding unto the said Apprentice

And for the true performance of all and every the said Covenants and Agreements either of the said Parties bindeth himself unto the other by these Presents In Witness whereof the Parties above named to these Indentures interchangeably have put their Hands and Seals the ___ day of ___ 1826 and in the ___ Year of the Reign of our Sovereign Lady ___ by the Grace of God of the United Kingdom of Great Britain and Ireland QUEEN Defender of the Faith and in the Year of our Lord One Thousand Eight Hundred and

Francis Tunley

John Bird

The Amount of the Money or the value of any other matter or thing given, or agreed to be given with the Apprentice by way of Premium must be truly inserted in words at length otherwise the Indenture will be void and double such amount or value forfeited.

Warrington & Co.

Shipwrights at Whites Conyer yard pre 1914, at the entrance to the saw pits. The saw sharpening horse can be seen bottom right.

Compare this with Harold Hinchley, son of the above, who served his time with Acorn Barge Building Company of Delce Wharf, Rochester from 1916-1923:

first year was   2 shillings a week
second year was   3 shillings a week
third year was   4 shillings a week
fourth year was   5 shillings a week
fifth year was   6 shillings a week
sixth year was   8 shillings a week
seventh year was 10 shillings a week

When Frank finished his apprenticeship with John Bird, he went into Chatham Dockyard. Both of his sons became shipwrights — Harold, who has already been mentioned, and Leslie.

Frank retired from the Dockyard in 1929 to enjoy nearly thirty years of retirement. He died in 1958, aged 89 years. Brian adds that, whilst checking the name Burt, he also checked the name Bird and learned that J. Bird was baptised 29th April 1832 at Chilham, Kent, son of William and Sara Bird.

ALFRED MARCONI WHITE

Alfred Marconi White was the son of Alfred White, who had the yard at Sittingbourne. A.M. White took over the Conyer Yard from John Bird in 1890. There was always great competition between father and son as to who built the fastest sailing barges.

S/B *Foxhound*. Note anchor hove well up — she could have been racing. (Books Afloat)

S/B *Foxhound*. She has too many people on board to be racing, perhaps a day out for the owner's employees?

(Books Afloat)

Alfred White senior started up a barge yard at Blackwall in the 1880s, where he built swim head barges for Goldsmith of Grays, Essex and it was at this yard that Alfred junior served his apprenticeship. In coming to Conyer, Alfred decided to build any type of barge such as swim heads, dumb and canal barges, as well as sailing barges. All his sailing barges can be traced but records of all other types have gone with the passing of time.

White's first barge was the *Herbert*, in 1890 of 43 tons. She was destroyed by bombs at Frindsbury in 1943. In the same year, he also built the *J.E.G.* of 44 tons. *J.E.G.* were the initials of J.E. Gill, for whom she was built. She was broken up at Rainham, Kent in 1949. White must have been busy on lighters the following years as no sailing barges were built.

In 1892 White's built *Tricolor* of 62 tons for Goldsmith's, which was still afloat at Battersea as a houseboat in 1960. She was followed by *Glendower* of 37 tons in 1893, and *Siola* of 54 tons in 1894, again for Goldsmith's. *Siola* was entered in the Barge Match of 1894 and was placed fourth. A second yard was opened in 1894 at Faversham, to help White cope with the vast amount of work he had on hand at the time. Conyer's next barge was the *Vendetta* of 55 tons followed by *Foxhound* of 56 tons, both in 1895. *Foxhound* was entered in the Thames Barge Match of 1928 and was placed third in the 'Rivers Bowsprit' class. Between 1910-11 *Foxhound* was burnt down to the waterline while carrying a load of petrol. She was re-built and

S/B *Iota*.   (Alan Cordell)

re-entered the Ramsgate Shipping and Hoy Company's service. *Foxhound* finished her days as a houseboat and was burnt at Oare Creek in 1955.

1896 saw the *Claxfield* 43 tons, named after a place just outside Lynsted, and the *Agnes* of 36 tons. The *Claxfield* was built for Mercer's of Teynham who had brickfields and farms and also a wharf at Conyer where they loaded bricks. In March 1934 she was lost off Yantlet, her crew being rescued by the Southend lifeboat. Three more barges were built in 1897. The *Alpha* 42 tons, built for Eastwood's who also had wharves at Conyer for their brickfields. She was a handy barge which Captain Howard sailed single-handed for almost two years. She was burnt at Otterham in 1950. Next came the *Madcap* 63 tons, built for Goldsmith's, and the *Satanita* 58 tons, also built for Goldsmith's, who entered her for both the Thames and the Medway Barge Matches of that year. She came first in the Medway and second in the Thames, a very fast barge with a good racing record. She was, however, to be involved in a tragic accident. The Whites, senior and junior, held a private race to see who had built the fastest barge. White senior entered the *Satanita* and three other barges entered to make a race of it. This was the first time a race had been held on a Sunday and was frowned upon by the more righteous people of the day. During the race *Victoria* was hit by a squall and capsized. Mr Austin, the owner, and Captain Webb were both drowned. The barge was towed to Northfleet, righted and eventually re-built.

1898 was a particularly busy year, no fewer than eight barges being built. The first was the *Kappa* of 39 tons, being built for Eastwood's and, after a

96

long hard life in the brick trade, she was broken up at Otterham in 1952. Next came the *Iota*, again for Eastwood's, also of 39 tons. She became a sailing yacht barge and finally a house barge on the Thames at Old Windsor. Next to be launched was the *Buckland* of 35 tons, built for Mercer and named after one of his farms. Later, she passed on to Smeed Dean's. The next barge was built on speculation. Not knowing what to call her, Alfred White took half his wife's name, Louisa, and half of his own and came up with *Loualf* and what a lovely name. Perhaps one of King Arthur's Knights, who all had such mellifluous names, should have been called this. She was 64 tons and, while under construction, was bought by Wilders and Carey of Essex. *Loualf's* launching safely afloat, the launching party then set off on a mad dash to Faversham where White had a second barge waiting to be launched at his Faversham Yard. This barge, *Dart*, also for Wilders and Carey, was launched by Mrs Wilder's granddaughter. In spite of having to launch both barges within a matter of an hour or so, the local newspaper reported that both launchings were most successful. The two barges were destined for the London River cement trade. Although she did have a race or two, the *Loualf* never came better than fifth. She became derelict in 1936 and was burnt at Murston in 1954.

The next launching at Conyer was the *Nesta* of 42 tons owned by Woods, brickmakers of Milton. She was a hulk in Milton Creek the last I saw of her, on the north bank of Ballast Wall Reach. She was followed by the *Lord Nelson* of 45 tons which was raced quite a lot. I know she had at least five second places but I cannot find any record of her ever coming first. She was later owned by Arthur Wenban of Sittingbourne who died aboard her in 1932 while fitting her out to follow that year's barge races with a number of local big wigs on board.

For this reason he wanted to put up a new 'bob' which his wife, who was in hospital at the time, had made for the barge. In order to put the spindle upon which the metal bob frame revolved in the topmast truck he was hoisting the topsail, so that he could climb up the hoops to reach the truck when he collapsed and died.

His widow later attributed this to her having sewn the bob onto the frame with green thread as she did not have any other colour readily available. Many people are superstitious of the colour green.

The *Lord Nelson* could claim to be the barge built in the shortest time; she was laid down, launched and raced in the space of six weeks. Before a barge could race, she had to carry at least three cargoes. This she undoubtedly did but what her cargoes were or how she carried them is anybody's guess. I have never been able to find out. Even I, who know something about barge building, find the feat incredible in such a short time. I have heard old barge builders talk about it and there is no doubt about it at all. There were a lot of shipwrights employed there at the time; all three freights could have been carried on the way to the race and could have been

Marconi with her anchor catted, probably racing in a stiff breeze. (Books Afloat)

A painting of *Victory*. (Alan Cordell)

any small object dropped off at somewhere like Queenborough and other places on the Thames.

Pioneer and *Protector* were the last two to be built that year of 1898. Both were of 64 tons and built for Edward Lloyd, the paper manufacturer of Sittingbourne. They lay derelict for some years and they were burnt together near the head of Milton Creek in 1966. Three more barges were built in 1899. *Northumberland* was the first. She was another Eastwood's barge of 43 tons. Worn out in the brick trade, she became a housebarge in 1945 and was broken up at Hoo in 1951. She was followed by the *Durham*, also for Eastwood's, of 42 tons. She was an unlucky barge, being cut down by a Dutch ship and sunk. The crew were saved and taken to Greenwich Hospital. She was salved and again, loaded with 40,000 bricks, she sat on the gridiron at Barking and sank again, only to be raised and again return to work. She became a mud barge, rigged with a lugsail and worked out of Halstow until 1957. She was hulked on Glass Bottle Beach and then broken up.

Next came the *Royal George* of 59 tons. She was built for the Ramsgate Hoy trade and, like most of the Conyer built barges, had a good turn of speed. She passed to the London & Rochester Trading Company. Her sails were removed in 1939 and, as a motor barge, she was sunk in collision in 1951 and broken up at Norton's Yard, East Greenwich in 1959.

In 1900 four barges were built. The *Sandown* of 44 tons was another local name and built for Mercer's. She was a house barge at Chatham in the early 1930s, derelict in 1957 and burnt two years later. Next came the well-known *Westmoreland* 43 tons, another of White's fast barges. She eventually became the property of the Thames Barge Sailing Club in 1963 and, after an expensive refit, got hooked up on a concrete lighter in the Medway. She had broken her bow section off. Some time later, Colin Frake, who had done so much work on her, bought the hulk and towed it to Faversham and, so far, has done a wonderful job in repairing her.

Westmoreland was followed by *Lancashire* of 43 tons. She was also built for Eastwood's and later sold to Wakeley's. She ended her days as a motor barge and was finally buried at Maldon. The last of that year's launchings was that of the *Rutland* of 36 tons, yet another one for Eastwood's 'County Class'. She was broken up at Whitewall Creek. 1901 saw three barges go down the slipways. The first of these was the *Warwick* of 36 tons and was launched by my aunt, Alice Austin, who was eleven years old at the time. *Warwick* was yet another barge for Eastwood's; she was laid up after the Second World War.

Alfred White used his second name for his next barge, the *Marconi* of 43 tons. She could, however, have been named in appreciation of the radio pioneer, Marconi. Although she was a fast barge she never seemed to do well in races and ended her days by being broken up at Ramsgate in 1946. *Victory* was next, of 44 tons. At one time she was owned by Mrs Mary

Olympia. Unknown wharf, Captain Douglas standing aft. His crew are all standing looking over the starboard bow.   (Miss Douglas)

Captain Douglas in his retirement and at the time when he was still at sea.   (Miss Douglas)

Pover of 54 Park Road, Faversham. She became a motor barge in 1946 and in 1960 was hulked in Shepherd's Creek. The year of glory for Alfred White must have been 1902 when he built his biggest sailing barge ever at Conyer, the *Olympia* of 97 tons, built for Colonel Honeyball of Newgardens, Teynham, farmer and coal merchant and perhaps one of the most important persons in Teynham at the time, whose coal business spread all over Kent.

The barge was ketch rigged and when I worked at the yard, George Gates, who managed it, told me that she was so long that she had ten feet of her protruding into the road outside of the shed.

The sheds are 90 feet long and, to this day, you can still see where the shed was cut out to allow the stem and 10 feet of the barge through to the edge of the road, which was only a flint road at the time, leading to the brickfields. On her launching, her stem head only just cleared the roof cross ties. She must have looked massive after the normal run of barges.

My Aunt Alice was at the launching and she told me that it was a nice bright day but cold enough for Mrs Honeyball to keep both hands in her muff. As Mrs Honeyball stepped up to name and launch the barge, which was named after herself, she handed the muff to her husband who promptly put both his hands into it and there they remained until the ceremony was over!

Olympia was not built for speed but to carry coal and her place of registration was Faversham. Over the years there has been speculation as to what happened to *Olympia*. I have now found out through ex-skipper, Bob Childs, a very good barge historian. *Olympia* was sunk in collision with the SS *Loughbrow* in a position two miles south of Deal Pier on 13th March 1918. *Olympia* was loaded with pitch. The *Loughbrow* was a coasting steamer of 691 tons gross and 24 feet laden draught, about 850 tons deadweight. *Olympia* was owned by Samuel West at the time and her master was Captain Douglas of Faversham; his brother was mate and there was a third hand.

After all these years, I have found Captain Douglas's daughter who has lived only four miles away from me all this time. Miss Douglas told me that her father and his crew had been home and had left to take the *Olympia* to Boulogne. That night, as she sat at home with her mother and the family, the door opened and in walked her father and his crew. Her mother remarked that it had been a quick trip and it was then that her father told them how he had been rescued from their sinking barge.

Miss Douglas is well over 80 years old but is still very alert. She loaned me some photographs — one of *Olympia*. You can just see her father near the wheel.

James and Ann of 42 tons was the first barge to be built in 1903. She was owned in Faversham most of her life by Horsford, then by Cremer. She sank three times in collision: in 1947; in 1949; and then as a motor barge was cut down off Erith in November 1952, cement laden out of Faversham.

Sara with bowsprit steeved up in one of the London Docks unknown to me.   (Books Afloat)

S/B *Ronald West*. Built at Conyer, photographed in Rye Harbour about 1936 by John L. Bowen, C.Eng., M.R.I.N.A.
(John L. Bowen)

The master and his wife were drowned. *Sara*, one of the best racers ever built, of 50 tons, was the next and, up to 1963, had been placed sixteen times first, ten times second and ten times third in the Thames and Medway Races. What a wonderful achievement, both for the barge and the crews, not forgetting the owners, who spent considerable sums of money in preparing their barge for the match. Everard's, the last owners, never sold her but broke her up themselves at Greenhithe in 1965, not wishing to part with her.

Next to be built was the *Ronald West* of 73 tons, built for Samuel West, designed for cargo carrying and not for racing. She was followed by *Toots* of 51 tons, built for W. Cunis who had a fleet of barges with peculiar names. *Torment*, also of 51 tons, was built next, again for Cunis. She was entered for that year's barge match and came third to *Sara* who was first, the *Garibaldi* being second. *Torment* was only beaten by two of the fastest barges that ever raced. It was also reckoned to be the best barge race on record. What a day it must have been for Alfred White to have had two of his barges in the first three.

1904 saw *Tam* of 41 tons and *Wumps* of 39 tons launched, built for W. Cunis. These were followed by *Resurga* of 50 tons built for Samuel West. For 1905, I can find no trace of any sailing barges being built. In 1906, the *K.C.* of 42 tons was the only one built. She finished up as a houseboat. In August 1962, Richard Sherren, a former actor, was fined £30 for taking *K.C.* in an unseaworthy condition from Greenwich to Felixstowe Ferry, which he denied. She was towed by a ballast barge.

1907 was an unlucky year for the yard. They had two barges being built when the sheds caught fire. They managed to save one and eventually launched it, the *Doddles* of 41 tons. Her sister which was too badly burned was the *Dawgy*. They were both for W. Cunis. Odd sounding names for barges, with due respect to the late W. Cunis. It has been suggested that they were nicknames of some of the Cunis family youngsters. After the fire the charred remains of *Dawgy* were pulled outside the sheds and remained there for years, a charred mass of timber. Following this disastrous year, they rebuilt the yard and were engaged on building two swim head lighters and dumb barges. In between, they did a lot of repair work and rebuilding. In 1912 *Doddles* capsized while crossing the Maplin Sands. She had on board a crew of three, all brothers aged 14 years, 18 years and 21 years; they were all drowned.

The year 1913 saw them again working on a sailing barge. This one, the *Ashingdon* of 59 tons, built just before the First World War, was for Miller's of Dartford. She was back in Conyer in the mid 30s for repairs, then owned by Peters until the early 50s. She was the last barge owned in Southend. She then was owned by Mrs Blackden's parents and, once again, had a link with Conyer. She was last heard of as a houseboat at Chiswick in 1970.

Annie Byford, the last trading barge built at Conyer. She is carrying an extra large staysail which is not having much effect on a windless day.   (Alan Cordell)

Defence Boom Blocks being built at Conyer during the First World War, built by Whites bargeyard shipwrights.

A newly launched canal barge at Whites, Conyer yard, 1936. (Mrs Crick)

War was declared in 1914 and this was to be the last year that sailing barges were built at Conyer. Two were built. The first was the *Joy* of 56 tons built for Rankin, the miller of Stambridge in Essex. She was sold for conversion to a yacht at Salcote in 1956 and, when last heard of, she was in the South of France.

The very last sailing barge built for trading was the *Annie Byford* of 54 tons, built for John Byford of Poplar. I worked on her in 1936 when she came back to Conyer for repairs and refit. She was eventually sunk at Erith, laden with cement. After the *Annie Byford* was launched, the barge yard was put on work for the Admiralty, making blocks for the submarine defence booms. These were baulks of timber bolted together to make cubes of about six feet. They were built on Richardson's Wharf and, when finished, were lifted into the water by Richardson's steam crane and towed away to Sheerness by tugs.

Work continued on lighters and canal boats for the Lee Conservancy. I can remember the names of the last ones built which were the *Enfield, Rye, Leyton* and *Latten*. These were followed by a swim head lighter which White built on speculation but he sold her before we had finished her, to a London Beer Company who named her *Expe*. We finished the *Expe* just as the Second World War started. We then came under the Ministry of Supply and built seven swim head canal barges for Waltham Abbey Explosive Works, the very last wooden barges built at Conyer. After the war, we had numerous barges in for motorising and a few for conversion to barge yachts. Going back to 1899, I have seen a record of White's building swim head lighters of 90 tons. These were big ones: the *Ladysmith, Mafeking, Kimberly* and *Belmont*. It is interesting to note the price of £695 each.

There were two barge yachts built there in the 1920s. One, the *Night Hawk*, was built for Mr Dawes. His son, Mr C.A.W. Dawes of Mount Ephraim, Faversham, gave me the history of this barge. I saw her advertised in 'The Times' as lying in Cannes, France, she being up for sale for about £16,000. She cost a few hundred to build. How's that for inflation? Mr Dawes saw her in France and he said she looked as good as the day she was built. She is described in 'Lloyds Register of Yachts' of 1931 as 'Official No.4187, Electric Light, built of Wood. Petrol Motor, Leeboards, Aux. Cutter Barge, 13.89 tons. 40.1 feet on water line. 11.5 feet breadth. 5 feet depth. Builders A.M. White & Co., Conyer Quay 1923. 6 cylinder Petrol Motor Ailsa Craig. Owner E.S. Dawes, Faversham'. From 'The Times', Thursday 2nd September 1980:

'Thames Barge for sale. Moored in Cannes. *Night Hawk* built by White & Co., Teynham, 1924. Entirely renovated: Length 40 feet. Traditional rigging: 80 hp Diesel engine: storage 1,200 litres fresh water & 300 litres fuel. Mooring rights in Cannes main harbour. £16,000 o.n.o.
Maitre Andre-Charles Blanc,
11 Place du Marchi, Porville,
06400 Cannes, France'

(Note the differing date of building).

The other barge yacht was the *Growler* built in 1922. I have very little information on her but would like to know if anyone has any. I must thank Mr Brian R. Woods for loaning me a letter which he had in his possession. Brian lives on Canvey Island, Essex and used to sail his gaff cutter, *Sea Mynx* to Conyer for many years. He had worked on *Growler* and knew her very well. *Growler* was built for T.H. Hughes. Tom Hughes was a great lover of tradition and insisted that *Growler* be built in the same manner and of the same materials as a Thames barge. It was only on the insistence of his brother that he agreed to have an auxiliary engine fitted. It was a 10 hp Ailsa Craig petrol/paraffin but he always maintained that he never used 'the stinking thing', preferring to use tide and sweeps; the sweeps being 16 feet long. Being his own boss, he was able to cruise around a great deal and the ship was well known in the estuary and Medway as well as up river as far as Gravesend. At the outbreak of war, *Growler* was laid up on her mooring opposite the Benfleet Yacht Club and remained there until she was purchased by E.E. Sugg in about 1946-47. She had suffered from not being used and her bottom was thick with weed. She was placed on blocks in Sam Hearn's yard and, with the aid of carefully placed coke fires, the bottom was dried. Vast quantities of weed, barnacles and surface wood — the bottom boards were elm — were scraped off and after further drying, boiling hot pitch and tar were applied. The mast was removed and it was found that the canvas gaiter had allowed water to penetrate between deck and mast, setting up a certain amount of rot. Frank Coleman scarfed a new section into the mast and this remained good to the day she was sold out of the Club some twenty or so years later.

The leeboards were allowed to drop into the mud by the mooring and, when dug out, they were quite sound and usable. The engine was found on the bank at the side of the Club gangway, covered in weeds and a rotten piece of canvas. It was stripped down and made to run out but, on being installed again, it was found to be quite inadequate and was replaced with a 20 hp Palmer which proved ideal. She was sold to Guy Welsh who enjoyed sailing in her for many years until ill health forced him to sell to Mike de Boltz who lavished a great deal of time and cash in restoring her to her original rig; just before the war, Tom Hughes had reduced her sail area quite considerably. She was sold and taken up the Deben where she is believed still to be although in a very neglected state.

EDWARD FISHER

Edward Fisher was probably the best known of the shipsmiths in the Swale area. Born in 1875, he was the son of a Whitstable seaman who sailed in the barquentines and brigantines out of Whitstable to the north for coal. Unfortunately, his father was washed overboard one terrible stormy day off the mouth of the Humber and was drowned.

Edward was always known as Ted Fisher and, at the age of 14, was apprenticed as a shipsmith with the Whitstable Shipping Company Limited, the firm his father worked for. His Indentures are dated 22nd Day of April 1889, the wages to be three shillings a week for the first year, three shillings and sixpence a week for the second year, four shillings a week for the sixth year and eight shillings a week for the seventh year.

From 1896, when he came out of his time, he probably worked at Whitstable until 1899 when he went to White's Conyer yard to work. He was married at Teynham Church on 1st June 1903 at the age of 28, taking up residence at Coastguard Cottages. In 1905, after six years with White's, work dried up at the Conyer yard and Ted left to get work at Cremer's Yard at Hollow Shore. During his stay at White's, he had produced the ironwork for nineteen new barges and much repair work for other barges. Ted had made ironwork for the fastest and biggest barges built at Conyer. Just look at the names: *Northumberland, Durham, Royal George, Sandown, Westmoreland, Lancashire, Rutland, Victory, Warwick, Marconi, Olympia, James and Ann, Sara, Ronald West, Torment, Toots, Resurga, Tam* and *Wumps.* Anyone would have been proud to have worked on these barges.

After leaving Conyer, Ted went to Cremer at Hollow Shore where the work was renewing and repairing Cremer's brick barges and, I suspect,

Ted Fisher, shipsmith, making a fishermans anchor. (Eddie Fisher)

Ted Fisher outside his forge at Cremer's Bargeyard, Hollow Shore. (E. Fisher)

Ted Fisher at his forge at Cremer's Bargeyard, Hollow Shore. (E. Fisher)

Ted Fisher, shipsmith.   (Eddie Fisher)

general work brought in from the brickfields. He designed and built a large winch for hauling out barges up their slipway.

Ted's son, the well known Faversham artist, Eddie Fisher, told me that his father returned to the Conyer yard later and also had two years at Goldsmith's yard at Grays in Essex, returning again to Hollow Shore in his old age to do two days a week, presumably to keep his hand in.

Eddie Fisher gave me a list of names of workmen at Hollow Shore at the time his father worked there: W. Gregory (Foreman), Perce Dadson, George Cole (who worked at Conyer with Ted Fisher), W. Clarke, Edward Fisher (shipsmith), T. Smith and Eddie Fisher.

Edward Thomas Fisher died on 16th December 1953 at the Kent & Canterbury Hospital, aged 78 years.

QUEENBOROUGH
One would think that Queenborough was ideally situated for barge building but that is not so, there being very little space left to establish a barge building yard even in the heyday of barge building. The yard that became established was in fact not in a good position as launching slips had to be laid across the road and the barges, when being launched, had to cross the road.

Cutters Dock where Nobby Wood had his barge repair yard at Queenborough.   (Author)

Today, this would cause havoc with the amount of traffic on even the least used of roads.

Very little is known about the builders at Queenborough. There seem to be no records and, although I enlisted the aid of the Clerk to Queenborough Parish Council, Mr Cackett, who gave me names and addresses, the people concerned were mostly too old to remember names — something I am beginning to find out as my memory plays tricks on me now — so, it was back to other methods of research. The earliest recorded barge I have is the *Queenborough*, built in 1855 of 36 registered tons. By 1881 she was in the fleet of Robert Mark Shrubsall, Milton, Kent and, by 1890 she was owned by James Gower of 11 New Norton Road, Hoxton, Middlesex and out of register by 1919.

In 1860 *Edward & Charles* was built of 47 tons and owned by George Mantle in 1881 and George West of Charlton, Kent in 1890. She finished up being owned by A.P.C.M. Ltd, London in 1919.

Next on record is the *Sara & Eliza*, built in 1863 of 35 tons. This barge was owned by Robert Watts of Sittingbourne in 1881 and, in 1890, was owned by Mr Goodenough, City of London. She was also out of the register by 1919.

Atalanta of 40 tons was built in 1865. By 1881 she was owned by James Bills, grazier, barge owner of High Street, Queenborough and in 1919 she was in the hands of Queenborough Lighterage Company Ltd, London.

1866 saw *Eliza* launched. Built by Edwin Burgess of Queenborough, of 35 tons, she was built for Charles Richardson of Conyer and launched by

Miss Beacon of Conyer on 26th June 1866. Edwin Burgess had taken over the yard in 1865 from Japter, James & Page. Whilst building the *Charles* of 36 tons in 1866, also for Charles Richardson, Edwin Burgess went bankrupt. He had underestimated badly. Sailing barge building seems to have occupied the twelve years between 1855 and 1867. Kelly's Directory of 1874 gives John Wright of South Street, Queenborough as a boat and barge builder. Kelly's Directory of 1895 gives no barge building activities and only one shipwright, John Thomas Berry, who probably worked in Sheerness Dockyard, William Ost, sailmaker and chandler and Edward Willder, boat builder of South Street.

It has always been somewhat of a mystery as to where the barge yard at Queenborough was situated so, to try to pin down the position, I decided to go and find out. My first call was at Nobby Wood's house which is opposite Cutters Dock where Nobby had his barge repair yard. After about two and a half hours talking, we decided to get a third opinion and it was arranged to get young Tom Schmid at a later date. 'Young Tom' is over eighty. Nobby Wood had worked on many barges in his yard at Cutters Dock. He had laid down blocks on the old bottom of SB *Monday*, which had made good hard standing. Many barges had motors installed on these blocks, quite a few had been converted to yacht barges and many others had been repaired there.

The day arrived when we were to meet Tom Schmid. Norman Fortune-Fowler, another ex-bargeman, drove me over to Queenborough and when we arrived Nobby, not having seen Norman for some years, greeted him in the usual barge talk terms by saying: 'Hello there, you ugly old bugger'. Nobby got a similar greeting from Norman, perhaps in stronger terms.

There was lots of talk before Tom Schmid arrived and then more greetings. After considerable conjecture, we were no nearer to making a decision as to the location of the barge yard so, Tom having been taken home by Norman, Nobby and I had a walk around to see both the suspected sites and we decided it could only have been the one shown in the photograph.

Nobby, being of an age when everyone says: 'Go and see Nobby, he'll tell you,' was one day approached by a well-known newspaper columnist. The columnist wanted to do an article on Dead Man's Island. After many pints in the local, Nobby agreed to take him by barge boat, a heavy-built, 14 foot boat that was always trailed or suspended in davits on sailing barges.

This newspaperman had already told that he was an ex-Oxford Blue so the rowing would be nothing to him. So, on the great day, they set off from Queenborough, the newspaperman, Nobby and others. Whilst Nobby steered the boat, they put the Blue on the oars and kept him rowing up and down the Swale, nowhere near Dead Man's Island, all the while telling him yarns about the big black hound dogs that roamed around and all sorts of other weird tales that they made up on the way. Finding a soft patch of mud, they told him to hop over the side and walk. He did just that but, instead of walking, he sank up to his waist in the mud. They let him struggle

The most probable place that barges were launched from at Queenborough. (Author)

for some time and then pulled him out. Eventually, they arrived back duly washed free of mud and the Oxford Blue went back to his newspaper. That week, his story about the black hounds of Dead Man's Island and other weird tales appeared in the national daily newspaper. There was an uproar at the local pub over this article, all the customers knowing that Nobby had taken the newspaperman to Dead Man's Island and Nobby and his friends decided to keep away from the pub for a day or two!

THE FAVERSHAM BUILDERS

The Faversham barge builders never matched the output of their neighbouring town of Sittingbourne which, of course, included Milton and Murston. I can think of lots of reasons for this although it would be difficult to put it down to any one in particular.

Faversham had been a very busy port for centuries and its ships, like Whitstable's, were mostly deep water vessels. During the mid-19th century sailing barges began to appear and, as early as 1824, Readman built the swim headed sailing barge *Harmony*. By 1850, the sailing barge was well established at Faversham. These sailing barges were between 70 and 80 feet long with a beam of 17 to 20 feet and a depth of between 5 and 6 feet. The early built sailing barges were for river work but the bigger coasting barges soon appeared and practically took over most of the cargoes into and out of Faversham.

One of the first barge builders was named Readman who, in 1824, built the *Harmony* of 24 tons. In 1826 he built the 33 ton *Providence* and the 36 ton *Commerce*. The *Gratitude* of 25 tons was built in 1838, followed by *Confidence* of 31 tons in the same year. In 1841, he built a very small barge, the *Two Sisters* of 10 tons. Later he built the *Industry* in 1851 and *Hero* in 1855, followed in 1857 by another *Harmony*. About this time, Mark Readman took over the running of the yard and, in 1862, he built the *Wave* and the *Susan* and the *Victoria* in 1864. In 1866 came three more, the *Pearl*, *Star* and the *Daisy*.

John Goldfinch was born at Deal in 1822. He came to Faversham around 1853 and started to build barges at the Coal Exchange Wharf in 1854. There had been a barge yard there before as a large hoy barge had been built there in 1825, named the *Royal Frederick*. It seems that Goldfinch's stay there was short as in 1857 he had his yard at the King's Head Quay, where he stayed for ten years before moving to Standard Quay where he built until 1894 when his son took over the yard. George Goldfinch continued to run the yard until around 1921.

The Goldfinches were reputed to have built some 47 sailing barges. I have not been able to trace all of them but some barges came off the register early in their life. One of John Goldfinch's early barges was the *Spy*, a single masted barge built in 1854. She loaded 120 tons and must have been built at the Coal Exchange Wharf. She was unlucky in being sunk twice and finished up as a lighter.

His first barge at the King's Head Quay was probably the *General Cathcart* of 1857 of 97 tons and schooner rigged. She was also wrecked in 1861 but the crew were saved. *Alice* of 44 tons was launched in 1859, *Garibaldi* also of 44 tons in 1861. *Monitor* was next in 1862, *Alabama* in 1863, *Fanny*, a swim head of 37 tons, also in 1863. In 1864 came the *Anne Maria* of 44 tons, which was at Conyer around the mid-thirties, lived on by Major Bellingham. The next year, the *Thames* was launched, followed by the *Medway* of 39 tons, *Teutonic* and the *Factor*, both of 37 tons and the *Brittania* of 42 tons. In 1867 two more barges were built, the *Phoenix* of 41 tons and the *Seagull* of 54 tons. I know of no barges being built in 1868 but this does not mean that none were built. In 1869 the *Tyne* of 41 tons was followed by the *Ann Goodhugh* in 1872, the *Ella* of 34 tons in 1874 and, the next year, the *Kent* of 27 tons, for the Cotton Powder Company and the *Pioneer* of 67 tons in 1876. In 1878 they launched the *Two Brothers* of 33 tons, the *Bessie Hiller* of 80 tons in 1881 and the *Cock Of The Walk* in 1882. Two more years were to pass before the next barge launch which was the *Pomona* of 52 tons. The *Economy* of 37 tons in 1885 was the only one that year, built for the Cotton Powder Company. Another three years were to pass before the *Alice* of 1888 was launched, the second one of that name to be built at the yard. 1890 saw the launching of the *Nancy*, a schooner rigged barge for the collier trade followed, in 1891, by the *Ellen-Jane* of

Hollow Shore bargeyard with a barge waiting in Oare Creek and a barge waiting in Faversham Creek. (J. Hunt)

The author (left) and Jeremy Nesham fitting chine doublings to Orinoco at Hollow Shore Bargeyard. (H. Perks)

S/B *Goldfinch* awaiting the tide in Faversham Creek.   (J. Hunt)

36 tons and the *Mersey* of 44 tons. The well known *Goldfinch* arrived in 1894. She was schooner rigged and 250 tons, one of only two barges to carry proper topsails. The last of Goldfinch's barges was the *Atlas* of 45 tons in 1894-5.

On the opposite bank of the creek to Goldfinch's was the yard of Anderson where, in 1894, Hilton Anderson and Brooks had the barge *Swale* built for them, presumably by or under the supervision of Alfred Marconi White of Conyer fame. This yard was soon to be taken over by White, whose yard at Conyer, although covered and having the capacity to build three barges at the same time, was not large enough for the output he was capable of. So, sometime between 1894 and 1895, White took over Anderson's yard at the Brents.

By 1899 he had launched two barges, the *Dart* of 39 tons followed by the *Gerald*. The following year came the *Esther* and, in the same year, the *Ethel* of 46 tons, later to be renamed the *Pride of Sheppey*. In 1901 he launched two more, the *Aubrey* of 72 tons and the *Nicholas* of 47 tons, his final barge being the *Beryl* of 76 tons which was later renamed *Santille*. White finished building between 1905 and 1906.

John Usher, who was probably the first builder of barges at Hollow Shore, was believed to have built at least seven barges, the earliest of which was the *E.A.R.L.* in 1854. In 1859, he built the *Black Boy* of 37 tons for Curtis and Harvey then, in 1866, the *Why Not*. Then there was a gap of seven years before the launch of the *William and Mary* of 45 tons, the *Empress*, later to be renamed *Scudd*, in 1877 and, in 1878, he built two; the

115

The Faversham-built S/B *Pretoria* being towed through the lockgate at Faversham by the
Faversham tug *Noni*.   (Author's collection)

S/B *Uplees* built at Uplees, awaiting the tide for launching. The people on deck are holding the tools of the trade. This is a good example of building out in the open. It seems to be a permanent site as the slipway is set up upon brick piers. The *Uplees* was taken to Chelsea for conversion to house barge in the summer of 1960. (John Cotton)

Return of 40 tons for Curtis and Harvey and the *Surprise* of 40 tons for the Cotton Powder Company.

The Hollow Shore yard, at the junction of Oare and Faversham Creeks, was owned by Cremer who, besides repairing his fleet of barges, built three good looking barges for his fleet; the *Nellie* and the *Bertie* both of 43 tons in 1901 followed by the *Pretoria* of 44 tons in 1902.

Osborn Dan owned a yard in the corner of the dock above the bridge at Faversham where he mostly did repairs to his fleet of barges but he still found time to build three barges there; the *Cecil Rhodes* in 1899, the *Baden Powell* of 47 tons in 1900 and the *Uplees* in 1897. The yard foreman was Mr Edwin Anderson and one of the shipwrights was Mr C. Denne.

Horsford also built a few barges, his yard being at Oare Creek. In 1879 he built three; the *Bethel* of 4 tons, the *H.R.A.* of 39 tons and the *Jane* of 38 tons.

Pollock's were the only other builders of sailing barges but they built in concrete and steel. During the First World War they built two concrete, three masted, schooner rigged barges with 120 hp Bolinder oil engines (centre screw), the *Violette* and the *Molliette* and also the *Bee*, which was built of steel and also had an engine fitted from new. She was built for Shepherd Brothers of Newport, Isle of Wight.

Lyford Anna at Purifier Dock, Faversham, in 1987. She sank here but later refloated herself. She looks sadly neglected now.

Lyford Anna ex *Cereal*.   (B.S. Longley)

Anderson Rigden & Perkins as it is today.   (Author)

WHITSTABLE

Over the years, Whitstable has had numerous shipyards, some of which built sailing barges and most of which repaired barges at some time during their existence.

Thomas Maddams, who was born in 1796, built barges and smacks at Whitstable between 1840 and the mid-1860s with the help of his son. He also kept the 'Shipwright's Arms' at Hollow Shore and ran the Hollow Shore barge yard for repairing barges. There is no evidence that he built any sailing barges there but he rebuilt a number of sailing barges including the *Imo*.

In 1847, there were a number of shipyards at Whitstable, some of which built sailing barges. Ship and barge builders listed in that year were:

James Daniels, who were also sailmakers

Thomas Gann, who were also sailmakers

James Hayward

Edward Holloway

Robert Young

John Graves and William Lott were listed as sailmakers only.

Twenty years later, in 1867, many new names appeared in the list of ship and barge builders:

Thomas Collar, ship and boat builder at Sea Wall

George Goldfinch, sailmaker

John Graves, sailmaker, the Sea Wall

Charles Hoult, mast and block maker, the Wall

William Hoult, sailmaker, the Wall

John Rogers, shipbuilders, Sea Wall

William Jutson, sailmaker

William Lawson, sailmaker, Harbour Terrace

James H. Lott, sailmaker, the Wall

William and Edward Holloway, shipbuilders

John Gann, shipbuilders and sailmakers

Gann's master sailmaker in 1860 was William Scott. Whitstable needed many sailmakers for the sailing colliers which usually blew out most of their sails in their rough passage from the North with coal for Whitstable. Other builders appear later, such as:

Solly (Harry Solly), whose yard later became R.J. Perkins, The Whitstable Shipping Co., who built at Gann's old yard, and, Anderson, Rigden & Perkins, who are still in existence.

On 21st July 1894 the Whitstable Shipping Company launched the 43 ton sailing barge *Cereal*, built for the firm's own hoy trade; at this time R. Perkins was the foreman shipwright. *Cereal* made a name for herself by capsizing in Whitstable Harbour when loaded with wheat and oats, doing no damage to herself. In 1949 she was converted as a barge yacht and is now owned by Mr B. Longley of Huckinge Court, Hollingbourne and is, at

Lyford Anna sadly neglected after being refloated in 1987.

S/B *Northdown* at Bridport. The date of this photograph is unknown, but by the look of the bus it could be in the 1930s. (Books Afloat)

present, moored in Faversham Creek. She was re-named *Lyford Anna* on becoming a barge yacht. She has since sunk in Faversham but is once again afloat.

Collar Brothers also engaged in barge work. They rebuilt the schooner barge *Alpha* on their slipway in 1893, the same slipway where, on 8th March 1862, Edward Molineux fell to the ground, a distance of 24 feet, when the staging around the brigantine *Ringleader* collapsed.

The spritsail barges were found to be cheap to run and easy to maintain so the cutter hoys were going out of favour, but the Whitstable hoy, *Good Intent*, was cut in two and lengthened and made into a brigantine called the *Tankerton Towers*.

The sailing barge, *Gozby Solly*, was rebuilt from the Ipswich built barge *Aveyron* at Solly's yard. Some new sailing barges built and launched at Whitstable by the Whitstable Shipping Company were the *Duluth* of 57 tons in 1895 and the *Eucrete* of 200 tons in 1913. The *Eucrete* was built with an engine.

In 1924 Anderson, Rigden & Perkins built the *Northdown*. Mr R.K. Anderson informed me that all the records were lost in a serious fire some thirty years ago. However, I well remember the *Northdown* being built and launched although I was not very old at the time. Originally she was to have been a much longer vessel, for use in the coal trade by my father. This trade fell off and some twenty feet was taken out of the bottom of *Northdown*, which was the only part completed, and she was duly sold to Burley for £2,100.

Spending an evening with Harold Rowden, B.E.M. and holder of a bronze medal for lifesaving at sea, we got to talking about barges. Harold had spent 59 years at sea, starting at twelve years of age. He had seen a lot of barges in those 59 years. He told me that the *Northdown* had been built almost twice. He then told me that when Perkins were building the *Northdown*, George Tabor wanted a twin-screw oyster fishing boat called the *Marmion*. They wanted it in a hurry and the only suitable seasoned timber in the yard was already in the partly-built *Northdown*, so they set to and pulled *Northdown* to pieces to build *Marmion*, rebuilding *Northdown* later. Harold was able to name some of the men working at the Perkins yard at the time.

Charles Perkins (foreman), George Perkins, George Richards, Harry Bill, Frank Payne, Mr Whorlow, George Fisher (blacksmith) and Sibert Perkins (blacksmith's mate). In addition to these names, Mr R.K. Anderson added: Charlie Perkins (nephew of Charles, the yard manager), A. Fox, A. Humphrey, W. Amos, E. Gisby, Norman Rigden, H. Beale, Toby Norris and C. (Champagne) Waters. No doubt there are some I have forgotten.

George Fisher, the shipsmith at Anderson, Rigden & Perkins, was the brother of Edward Fisher, the shipsmith at Conyer and Hollow Shore.

121

Northdown at Burley's Dolphin Yard fitting out for the 1935 Barge Matches.   (Jack Sindry)

Eddie Fisher, the son of Edward, told me that, at one time when work was short, his father had agreed to go to White's yard at Faversham. George, also being without work, needed a job as he had a family to support, whereas Edward did not. Consequently, Edward asked White if he would take his brother George instead. White agreed and then Edward went on Rigden's diving boat to the Scheldt, working on a wreck.

The largest barge ever built at Whitstable was the *Nellie-S*, built by H.H. Gann & Co. at their West Beach Yard in 1876. She was 131 feet in length, 26 feet in breadth and carried 520 tons on a draft of 12 feet 6 inches. She was barquentine rigged. Dick Perkins was foreman shipwright. The barge was put into the South American trade.

H.H. Gann & Co., besides being builders, were also owners. At one time, their fleet numbered over twenty ships. Around 1870 Gann had built the barquentine rigged barge *Zebrina*, which was still in the coal trade in the 1930s and was still working, with an engine installed, in 1938. She was 109 feet long by 24 feet wide and of 160 tons. She had squared chines, the same as a spritsail barge, but never carried leeboards. At one time, the *Zebrina* came into the hands of the Whitstable Shipping Company and, in 1895, they built a sister ship to the *Zebrina* and named it *Belmont*. In the 1930s she was re-named Camber. She was 104 feet long by 24 feet beam and of 149 tons.

THE *WESTMORELAND* SAGA

Westmoreland was a pretty little barge of 43 tons. In her time she had worked hard in the brick trade, attending barge matches whenever possible and making a name for herself as a fast barge, winning (as a trading barge) five times and being placed second and third many times. In 1963 she became the property of the Thames Barge Sailing Club. In August 1973, after having an expensive refit, she managed to get hooked up on a concrete lighter at Hoo on the Medway. As the tide receded, her bow section broke off completely. She was stripped of her gear and taken to the saltings at Hoo and left.

About a year later Colin Frake, who had spent many hours of voluntary work on her, asked me if it would be possible to tow her to Faversham. We decided that if she had a dam built across her, just aft of where her bow section had been broken off, it would be possible to tow her stern first, which is just what Colin did. The following Easter, with the help of Alan Reekie and his sailing barge, *Ironsides*, the tow was successfully completed and she was berthed close to the place where Goldsmith's had their barge building yard. It was by no means a good berth, in fact, it could not have been worse for what Colin was about to undertake: the building on of a new bow section, which would normally be carried out in a building sheltered from the weather. There was no such place available and, if there had been, I am sure Colin would not have been able to afford it.

The modern 'Pit Sawyer' at work.

One task complete: the stem fitted.

Colin Frake deep in thought beside his new acquisition, the wreck of the *Westmoreland*.

Battens now in place, ready to fit the frames.

Some time later Colin rang me and asked me to meet him at the barge. He was worried about the barge which had a very distinct twist caused by the bad berth. As there was no chance of a better berth, we worked out between us that it would be possible to build the amount of twist into the new section and hope that it would eventually right itself, which it did.

Colin was a very determined man who had made up his mind to somehow save this barge which his father, Charles Frake, had skippered many times. I came away thinking what a task Colin had taken on and wondering whether or not I would have taken it on when I was younger. For a start, he had to try to save what he had got, covering up with sheets to stop rainwater getting in and tidying up the ragged ends where she had broken off — a considerable job in itself and, of course, time consuming when time was at a premium. In addition, he had a job which meant that he only had weekends to work on her. It is well over a decade now since Colin started to work on *Westmoreland* and she is still far from finished.

Eventually, it came to timber supplies and Colin found it cheaper to buy it in Hull from a firm called Barchard's than it was to buy locally. They had some at 27 feet in length. The timber arrived and was duly stacked in the proper manner to season a little before use. In spite of this, it warped and twisted so he did the old trick of throwing it in the creek which kept it from twisting and just dragged out a plank whenever he needed one. Colin has

Westmoreland in her Faversham berth.

since told me that the oak is now very hard which is a good thing, showing that it has seasoned well. He told me he remembered me telling him that we planked up some of our swim head lighters with a double skin of English larch so he bought some and found it much easier to work. I would estimate that there has been five tons of timber, or even more, put into *Westmoreland* up to now, mostly made up of the stem apron, stem, floors and frames which are all cut from flitches — timber over five inches thick.

Joining up the new work underneath the barge's bottom required the removal of tons of mud, to allow one to get under the barge to fasten the planks together. This done, it had to be shored up to stop it slipping which could, of course, be very dangerous. Colin built himself a steam chest to steam his planks prior to bending them on. I was very glad to see that he had made the take-over joint correctly; if done badly, it is a constant source of trouble with leaks. Apart from the damage to the bow, Colin has had to put in new sailing beams which he has made up with steel and perhaps some of the foredeck will also be steel.

The whole of this operation has been almost a one-man job, although he has had some help from time to time. At the moment, Colin is very busy as a blockmaker of some repute and, therefore, he has less time to work on *Westmoreland*. What a wonderful wife he has, sharing him with his other love!

Chapter V:
Conclusion

The decline of the sailing barge has taken many years; her sisters, the schooners and smacks, faded away slowly; they too had a long and hard life. The coming of the sailing barge was partly to blame. The fact that she needed only a small crew was a very good reason in a time when even the large square rigged ships were sailing the oceans of the world with half a crew for the sake of economy. Another reason why the sailing barge evolved rapidly was her shallow draft and flat bottom, enabling her to sail into many of the shallow creeks and rivers where she could, if there was no wind, drift in with the tide and, having a flat bottom, could sit on the mud almost anywhere. All these benefits, plus the fact that she was cheap to build, made the sailing barge a desirable investment and companies whose products were made near water built up large fleets to convey their products to all parts of the British Isles and to other European ports.

Up until the Second World War there were still some considerable fleets working, especially in the brick, cement and grain trades. During the war many of these barges were taken over by the government, anchored in strategic places, with a barrage balloon attached to them, where they languished for six years. The fact that they had not had a coat of paint for some years prior to being requisitioned, plus the six years of war, transformed them into, in many cases, irreparable hulks. Many also became victims of war. The fact that many of the sailing barges traded to London ensured that a percentage would be lost to enemy action, not only by bombs but by floating mines dropped by enemy aircraft.

Many other factors combined to contribute to the decline of the sailing barge. Many owners replaced their barges with new motor coasters. In some cases the sailing gear was taken out and replaced with motors — a job that I was to do many times before I left the trade.

The end was slow in coming. One or two were still trading when a new lease of life became apparent. Some of the sailing barges had been used as lighters after having their gear removed. These were now coming on to the market and some were bought to convert to homes to relieve the housing shortage, others were bought to be rigged by enthusiasts, many of whom wanted to sail in the revived barge matches. A few large companies bought some of the larger barges and spent small fortunes, refitting them for the firm's use for such events as board meetings and business functions. These also entered the barge matches and were kept in very good condition, with new sails and rigging. Many others were bought by individuals and re-rigged with what could be found in the second-hand market which, in many cases, had been stored for years, much of it in good condition. Albert Groom, whose life revolved around antiques, had bought four sailing barges, three of which he rigged. He chartered these but told me he lost money doing so but he enjoyed sailing on one or other of them and liked to see them at a barge match. Most of the barges which did charter work had paid crews aboard and, when racing, expected the charterers to give a hand with pulling on ropes and winding winches.

It was people like these who showed such enthusiasm that has kept the sailing barges afloat and sailing today. How much longer these dear old ladies will be seen sailing around our coast cannot be foretold as they have a record of longevity; like the *Oak*. In the summer of 1987 I sailed her for the first time and found her to handle perfectly. My thanks to Benny and Joy Bensted. Benny, with the help of Don Grover, has practically rebuilt her over the years. Don Grover worked as a barge builder before going into working barges and is now the regular skipper of *Oak*.

The *Cambria*, the last sailing barge to trade under sail alone, is now at the Dolphin Museum, almost too far gone to be rebuilt for sailing again — the result of lying in St Katharine's Dock under the care of the Maritime Trust who had sadly neglected her to a point where they were about to drag her ashore and cut a hole in her side and let people walk in and look around. It was about this time that I was asked to go to London and survey her with the idea that we might have her at Sittingbourne's Dolphin Museum as an exhibit. I was saddened by the sight of her lying there with grass growing out of her joints, decks peeling of their paint, pumps running permanently to keep her afloat. A meeting there with the Maritime Trust assured me that money and help would be forthcoming to help to repair her. Little has been done at the moment except to keep out the rain.

When it was known that she was coming to Sittingbourne, a writer for one of the barge journals wrote to the effect that another barge was going to her doom by going to the Dolphin Museum — with reference to another barge given to us which had been far beyond repair. Now, I am trying to put the record right before the writer pens another article. First and foremost, when we are given old barges they are usually beyond repair and the donor is trying to get rid of what could be an expensive liability by donating it to the Museum. Secondly, the only finance we have is what we take in entrance fees; we are all volunteers and I cannot record the writer ever sending us a donation or volunteering to come to work on the barges. For his and any-one else's information, *Cambria* is still the property of the Maritime Trust so, if she falls to pieces, the Dolphin Museum will not be wholly to blame.

I have often been asked if it would be possible to build a new barge. My answer is always 'Yes, if anyone can afford to.' About 1968 I did a costing. I forget what the figure was but I do know that it frightened the person who asked me to do it. It also made me think and I decided that there were not many people who could afford to have a new barge built. Today is a different situation and I never cease to be amazed at the amount of money some people accumulate.

The barge builder will soon be extinct. There are some good tradesmen who are repairing sailing barges and making a good job of it. Then there are the bodgers who do the barge more harm than good — fortunately, they are few in number. Travelling around, I sometimes come across a barge being repaired. Naturally, I like to have a look at the job in hand; I may learn something. No two people do the same job in the same way. I am very often surprised at how good some of these untrained men are. Other times I have seen a job being murdered because the men have no idea how it should be done. I once offered some friendly advice and was promptly told to 'Shove off, what do you know about it?' That taught me a lesson not to interfere. On the other hand, I have had people come to me and seek information which has been readily given.

Shipwrights, in my opinion, were a strange lot, including myself. When building or repairing a barge, they would swear and curse about her the whole time they worked on her yet, when she was finished and leaving the yard, they would often say that they were sorry to see the lovely old lady go, wishing her all sorts of luck. I, myself, often felt that part of me was going with her and that I would probably never see her again. The skippers sometimes had a much different opinion of the barge.

Will there be some other vessel to take the place of the sailing barge when the last of them are gone, whenever that may be? They are a long-lived vessel but very expensive to keep in repair and to run; they are also very expensive to insure. Chartering helped to pay for all this but it looks as if one or two may be giving up on the chartering. There seems to be less and less chartering every year. Several things contribute to this. Our weather is probably the main cause; continuous rain, gale force winds, no wind at all. All these things put people off chartering for ever. Most people who charter do so because they like to sail; being cooped down below on a wet day or on deck in oilskins is not much fun when set against the price that they have to pay. A number of people now charter for day trips — this is not so bad as if it rains they have only lost one day.

It was on one of these day trips that I was invited to sail on *Oak*, now over 100 years old. *Oak* belongs to Benny and Joy Bensted and is skippered by Don Grover. We left Whitstable harbour in a dead flat calm and motored out about a mile when a ripple told us that we may have a breeze. We set all sail, therefore, and by the time we had tidied all the ropes up there was a nice breeze blowing. I was asked if I would like to take the wheel which I did in a flash. *Oak* was one of the barges that I had never sailed before and it

129

was a pleasant surprise to find that she handled beautifully with none of the unpleasant quirks which some barges have. It was a real pleasure to be engaged with this endearing old lady of the sea. I feel indebted to the Bensteds for the chance to sail their barge. The day turned out to be one of those perfect days that charterers wish for. The sun came out, sandwiches, beer and wine were brought on deck and everyone felt at peace with the world. I did wonder how many of those on board realised that they were sailing on a vessel over a hundred years old.

Oak has been extensively rebuilt and every year new problems arise and are overcome by much hard work from Benny, Joy and Don Grover. Don was a barge builder in his youth and still practises his trade when not sailing. Many good barges have had very much shorter lives than *Oak*, too many to write about here; some destroyed by human error, some by storms, fire or collision, some just sank for no apparent reason, probably through hitting an underwater object.

The shipwright's life was not an easy one. There were very few easy or light jobs. They became very fit, always rushing around trying to complete the contract in under the time, so as to earn themselves a small bonus. I started work at five shillings, less twopence National Health Insurance, for a week of 52 hours. In spite of this, there were no clock watchers and if a plank was being fastened off at knock-off time, everyone stopped until it was finished. In spite of this, I think people were more dedicated to their work; maybe the reason why sailing barges lasted so long.

Will we ever again see the likes of these craftsmen or the craft they built?